*Infinity Prime* Donna Casey

"This fractal is a classic spiral, which is my favorite, and I'm always amazed at the variations and the endlessly repeating patterns that can be created out of such a primary shape." – **Donna Casey**

# Investigations
### IN NUMBER, DATA, AND SPACE®

**Editorial offices:** Glenview, Illinois • Parsippany, New Jersey • New York, New York
**Sales offices:** Boston, Massachusetts • Duluth, Georgia
Glenview, Illinois • Coppell, Texas • Sacramento, California • Mesa, Arizona

scottforesman.com

The Investigations curriculum was developed by TERC, Cambridge, MA.

This material is based on work supported by the National Science Foundation ("NSF") under Grant No. ESI-0095450. Any opinions, findings, and conclusions or recommendations expressed in this material are those of the author(s) and do not necessarily reflect the views of the National Science Foundation.

ISBN: 0-328-23721-3

ISBN: 978-0-328-23721-0

**Second Edition Copyright © 2008 Pearson Education, Inc.**
All Rights Reserved. Printed in the United States of America. This publication is protected by Copyright, and permission should be obtained from the publisher prior to any prohibited reproduction, storage in a retrieval system, or transmission in any form by any means, electronic, mechanical, photocopying, recording, or otherwise. For information regarding permission(s), write to: Permissions Department, Scott Foresman, 1900 East Lake Avenue, Glenview, Illinois 60025.

5 6 7 8 9 10-V003-15 14 13 12 11 10 09 08 07

CC:N1

**TERC**

## Co-Principal Investigators

Susan Jo Russell

Karen Economopoulos

## Authors

Lucy Wittenberg
Director Grades 3–5

Karen Economopoulos
Director Grades K–2

Virginia Bastable
(SummerMath for Teachers,
Mt. Holyoke College)

Katie Hickey Bloomfield

Keith Cochran

Darrell Earnest

Arusha Hollister

Nancy Horowitz

Erin Leidl

Megan Murray

Young Oh

Beth W. Perry

Susan Jo Russell

Deborah Schifter
(Education
Development Center)

Kathy Sillman

## Administrative Staff

Amy Taber
Project Manager

Beth Bergeron

Lorraine Brooks

Emi Fujiwara

## Contributing Authors

Denise Baumann

Jennifer DiBrienza

Hollee Freeman

Paula Hooper

Jan Mokros

Stephen Monk
(University of Washington)

Mary Beth O'Connor

Judy Storeygard

Cornelia Tierney

Elizabeth Van Cleef

Carol Wright

## Technology

Jim Hammerman

## Classroom Field Work

Amy Appell

Rachel E. Davis

Traci Higgins

Julia Thompson

## Collaborating Teachers

This group of dedicated teachers carried out extensive field testing in their classrooms, met regularly to discuss issues of teaching and learning mathematics, provided feedback to staff, welcomed staff into their classrooms to document students' work, and contributed both suggestions and written material that has been incorporated into the curriculum.

Bethany Altchek

Linda Amaral

Kimberly Beauregard

Barbara Bernard

Nancy Buell

Rose Christiansen

Chris Colbath-Hess

Lisette Colon

Kim Cook

Frances Cooper

Kathleen Drew

Rebeka Eston Salemi

Thomas Fisher

Michael Flynn

Holly Ghazey

Susan Gillis

Danielle Harrington

Elaine Herzog

Francine Hiller

Kirsten Lee Howard

Liliana Klass

Leslie Kramer

Melissa Lee Andrichak

Kelley Lee Sadowski

Jennifer Levitan

Mary Lou LoVecchio

Kristen McEnaney

Maura McGrail

Kathe Millett

Florence Molyneaux

Amy Monkiewicz

Elizabeth Monopoli

Carol Murray

Robyn Musser

Christine Norrman

Deborah O'Brien

Timothy O'Connor

Anne Marie O'Reilly

Mark Paige

Margaret Riddle

Karen Schweitzer

Elisabeth Seyferth

Susan Smith

Debra Sorvillo

Shoshanah Starr

Janice Szymaszek

Karen Tobin

JoAnn Trauschke

Ana Vaisenstein

Yvonne Watson

Michelle Woods

Mary Wright

Note: Unless otherwise noted, all contributors listed above were staff of the Education Research Collaborative at TERC during their work on the curriculum. Other affiliations during the time of development are listed.

## Advisors

Deborah Lowenberg Ball,
University of Michigan

Hyman Bass, Professor of Mathematics and Mathematics Education
University of Michigan

Mary Canner, Principal, Natick Public Schools

Thomas Carpenter, Professor of Curriculum and Instruction,
University of Wisconsin-Madison

Janis Freckmann, Elementary Mathematics Coordinator,
Milwaukee Public Schools

Lynne Godfrey, Mathematics Coach,
Cambridge Public Schools

Ginger Hanlon, Instructional Specialist in Mathematics,
New York City Public Schools

DeAnn Huinker, Director, Center for Mathematics and
Science Education Research, University of Wisconsin-Milwaukee

James Kaput, Professor of Mathematics, University of
Massachusetts-Dartmouth

Kate Kline, Associate Professor, Department of Mathematics
and Statistics, Western Michigan University

Jim Lewis, Professor of Mathematics,
University of Nebraska-Lincoln

William McCallum, Professior of Mathematics,
University of Arizona

Harriet Pollatsek, Professor of Mathematics,
Mount Holyoke College

Debra Shein-Gerson, Elementary Mathematics Specialist,
Weston Public Schools

Gary Shevell, Assistant Principal,
New York City Public Schools

Liz Sweeney, Elementary Math Department,
Boston Public Schools

Lucy West, Consultant, Metamorphosis:
Teaching Learning Communities, Inc.

This revision of the curriculum was built on the work of the many authors who contributed to the first edition (published between 1994 and 1998). We acknowledge the critical contributions of these authors in developing the content and pedagogy of *Investigations*:

## Authors

Joan Akers

Michael T. Battista

Douglas H. Clements

Karen Economopoulos

Marlene Kliman

Jan Mokros

Megan Murray

Ricardo Nemirovsky

Andee Rubin

Susan Jo Russell

Cornelia Tierney

## Contributing Authors

Mary Berle-Carman

Rebecca B. Corwin

Rebeka Eston

Claryce Evans

Anne Goodrow

Cliff Konold

Chris Mainhart

Sue McMillen

Jerrie Moffet

Tracy Noble

Kim O'Neil

Mark Ogonowski

Julie Sarama

Amy Shulman Weinberg

Margie Singer

Virginia Woolley

Tracey Wright

# Contents

## U N I T   2

# Counting and Comparing

# Investigations

## Overview of Program Components

### FOR TEACHERS

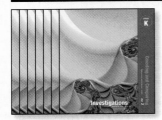

The **Curriculum Units** are the teaching guides. (See far right.)

**Implementing Investigations in Kindergarten** offers suggestions for implementing the curriculum. It also contains a comprehensive index.

The **Resources Binder** contains all the Resource Masters that support instruction. (Also available on CD) The binder also includes a student software CD.

### FOR STUDENTS

The **Student Activity Book** contains the consumable student pages (Recording Sheets, Homework, Practice, and so on).

The **Student Math Handbook Flip Chart** contains pictures of Math Words and Ideas pages.

## The *Investigations* Curriculum

*Investigations in Number, Data, and Space*® is a K–5 mathematics curriculum designed to engage students in making sense of mathematical ideas. Six major goals guided the development of the *Investigations in Number, Data, and Space*® curriculum. The curriculum is designed to:

- Support students to make sense of mathematics and learn that they can be mathematical thinkers

- Focus on computational fluency with whole numbers as a major goal of the elementary grades

- Provide substantive work in important areas of mathematics—rational numbers, geometry, measurement, data, and early algebra—and connections among them

- Emphasize reasoning about mathematical ideas

- Communicate mathematics content and pedagogy to teachers

- Engage the range of learners in understanding mathematics

Underlying these goals are three guiding principles that are touchstones for the *Investigations* team as we approach both students and teachers as agents of their own learning:

1. *Students have mathematical ideas.* Students come to school with ideas about numbers, shapes, measurements, patterns, and data. If given the opportunity to learn in an environment that stresses making sense of mathematics, students build on the ideas they already have and learn about new mathematics they have never encountered. Students learn that they are capable of having mathematical ideas, applying what they know to new situations, and thinking and reasoning about unfamiliar problems.

2. *Teachers are engaged in ongoing learning* about mathematics content, pedagogy, and student learning. The curriculum provides material for professional development, to be used by teachers individually or in groups, that supports teachers' continued learning as they use the curriculum over several years. The *Investigations* curriculum materials are designed as much to be a dialogue with teachers as to be a core of content for students.

3. *Teachers collaborate with the students and curriculum materials* to create the curriculum as enacted in the classroom. The only way for a good curriculum to be used well is for teachers to be active participants in implementing it. Teachers use the curriculum to maintain a clear, focused, and coherent agenda for mathematics teaching. At the same time, they observe and listen carefully to students, try to understand how they are thinking, and make teaching decisions based on these observations.

*Investigations* is based on experience from research and practice, including field testing that involved documentation of thousands of hours in classrooms, observations of students, input from teachers, and analysis of student work. As a result, the curriculum addresses the learning needs of real students in a wide range of classrooms and communities. The investigations are carefully designed to invite all students into mathematics—girls and boys; members of diverse cultural, ethnic, and language groups; and students with a wide variety of strengths, needs, and interests.

Based on this extensive classroom testing, the curriculum takes seriously the time students need to develop a strong conceptual foundation and skills based on that foundation. Each curriculum unit focuses on an area of content in depth, providing time for students to develop and practice ideas across a variety of activities and contexts that build on each other. Daily guidelines for time spent on class sessions, Classroom Routines (K–3), and Ten-Minute Math (3–5) reflect the commitment to devoting adequate time to mathematics in each school day.

# About This Curriculum Unit

This **Curriculum Unit** is one of seven teaching guides in Grade K. The second unit in Grade K is *Counting and Comparing.*

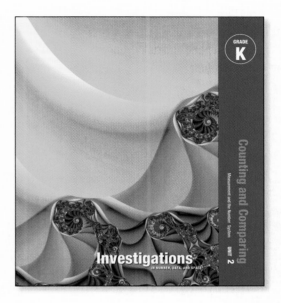

- The **Introduction and Overview** section organizes and presents the instructional materials, provides background information, and highlights important features specific to this unit.

- Each Curriculum Unit contains several **Investigations.** Each Investigation focuses on a set of related mathematical ideas.

- Investigations are divided into 30–45 minute **Sessions,** or lessons.

- Sessions have a combination of these parts: **Activity, Discussion, Math Workshop,** and **Session Follow-Up.**

- Each session also has one or more **Classroom Routines** that are done outside of math time.

- At the back of the book is a collection of **Teacher Notes** and **Dialogue Boxes** that provide professional development related to the unit.

- Also included at the back of the book are the **Student Math Handbook Flip Chart** pages for this unit.

- The **Index** provides a way to look up important words or terms.

# Overview

## O F   T H I S   U N I T

| Investigation | Session | Day | |
|---|---|---|---|
| **INVESTIGATION 1**<br>**Counting**<br>Students practice counting and connecting number words, numerals, and quantities. | **1.1** A Counting Book | 1 | |
| | **1.2** Grab and Count | 2 | |
| | **1.3** Counting Jar | 3 | |
| | **1.4** Roll and Record | 4 | |
| | **1.5** How Did I Count? | 5 | |
| | **1.6** Does Order Matter When You Count? | 6 | |
| | **1.7** Build It | 7 | |
| | **1.8** Counting Jar | 8 | |
| | **1.9** Inventories | 9 | |
| | **1.10** Strategies for Accurate Counting | 10 | |
| **INVESTIGATION 2**<br>**Comparing**<br>Students compare the length of objects and the quantities of different sets. They also practice ordering by length and quantity. | **2.1** Measurement Towers | 11 | |
| | **2.2** How Did You Measure? | 12 | |
| | **2.3** Counting Backwards | 13 | |
| | **2.4** Grab and Count: Compare | 14 | |
| | **2.5** The Game of Compare | 15 | |
| | **2.6** Comparing Two Inventory Bags | 16 | |
| | **2.7** Letters in Our Names | 17 | |
| | **2.8** Counting Jar | 18 | |
| | **2.9** Comparing Names | 19 | |
| | **2.10** Grab and Count: Ordering | 20 | |
| | **2.11** Ordering Names | 21 | |
| | **2.12** Ordering Cards | 22 | |
| | **2.13** End-of-Unit Assessment and Ordering | 23 | |
| | **2.14** End-of-Unit Assessment and Ordering Our Names | 24 | |

Each *Investigations* session has some combination of these four parts: **Activity, Discussion, Math Workshop,** and **Session Follow-Up.** These session parts are indicated in the chart below. Each session also has one or more **Classroom Routines** that are done outside of math time.

| Activity | Discussion | Math Workshop | Assessment Checklist* | Session Follow-Up |
|---|---|---|---|---|
| ●●● | ● |  | ● | ● |
| ● | ● | ● |  | ● |
| ● | ● | ● |  | ● |
| ●● | ● |  |  | ● |
|  | ● | ● |  | ● |
|  | ● | ● |  | ● |
| ● | ● | ● |  | ● |
| ● | ● | ● |  | ● |
| ●● | ● |  |  | ● |
|  | ● | ● |  | ● |
| ●● | ● | ● | ● | ● |
|  | ● | ● |  | ● |
|  | ● |  |  | ● |
| ● | ● | ● | ● | ● |
| ●● | ● |  |  | ● |
| ● | ● | ● |  | ● |
| ●● | ● | ● |  | ● |
| ● | ● | ● |  | ● |
| ● | ● | ● |  | ● |
| ● | ● | ● |  | ● |
| ● | ● | ● |  | ● |
| ● | ● | ● |  | ● |
|  | ● | ● |  | ● |
|  | ● | ● |  | ● |

**Classroom Routines**

| Calendar | Attendance | Today's Question |
|---|---|---|
| ● |  |  |
|  | ● |  |
|  |  | ● |
| ● |  |  |
|  | ● |  |
|  |  | ● |
| ● |  |  |
|  | ● |  |
|  |  | ● |
| ● |  |  |
|  | ● |  |
|  |  | ● |
| ● |  |  |
|  | ● |  |
|  |  | ● |
| ● |  |  |
|  | ● |  |
|  |  | ● |
| ● |  |  |
|  | ● |  |
|  |  | ● |

*An Assessment Checklist is introduced in this session.

# Mathematics

**Counting and Comparing** is the second of seven units in the Kindergarten sequence and the first of three units in the Kindergarten number strand. These units develop ideas about counting and quantity, comparison, linear measurement, the composition of numbers, and the operations of addition and subtraction. The mathematical focus of this unit is on giving students many meaningful opportunities to develop their sense of numbers and quantities, to count and compare amounts, and to measure objects by comparing them directly.

**LOOKING BACK**

This unit builds on the work in *Who Is in School Today?*. The routines introduced in that unit (*Attendance, Calendar,* and *Today's Question*) are done on a regular basis outside math time. Each provides practice with counting. They also provide experience with the calendar as a tool for keeping track of time and with collecting, counting, comparing, and looking at data. Students revisit the Counting Jar several times and begin to use the materials they freely explored in that unit for a mathematical purpose.

**This unit focuses on 5 Mathematical Emphases:**

## 1 Counting and Quantity Developing strategies for accurately counting a set of objects by ones

### Math Focus Points

◆ Developing strategies for accurately counting and keeping track of quantities up to 12

◆ Connecting number words, numerals, and quantities

◆ Developing visual images for quantities up to 6

◆ Counting backwards

Counting is the basis for understanding our number system and for almost all of the number work in the primary grades. Students in the same class vary considerably in age and in their previous experience with numbers and counting; therefore, expect a wide range of understandings. Many students entering Kindergarten may know the oral counting sequence up to 5, 10, or much higher; but they will vary tremendously in their ability to accurately count out a set of objects and in their sense of the size of quantities. Many are just beginning to explore the ways in which numbers give information about quantities of real things.

The work in this unit provides an introduction to and practice with many of the important aspects of counting. Students hear and use the counting sequence (the number names, in order) in a variety of contexts. They have many opportunities to connect the number names with the written numbers and with the quantities they represent.

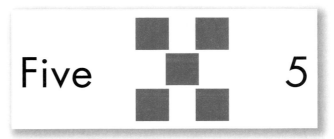
Five                    5

They have repeated experience with counting sets of objects and creating (and drawing) sets of a given size, which helps them see the importance of counting each object once and only once and of having a system for keeping track of what has been counted and what still remains to be counted.

## 2 Counting and Quantity Developing the idea of equivalence

### Math Focus Points

- Creating an equivalent set

- Considering whether order matters when you count

Students also begin an ongoing, year-long conversation about equivalence that is, in part, algebraic in nature. In this unit, the focus is on whether organization and order matter when you count. For example, are the sets in Figure 1 the same or does one have more? Does it matter if you count the yellow squares or the red squares in Figure 2 first? For more information about equivalence, see **Algebra Connections in This Unit,** page 16.

*Figure 1*

*Figure 2*

## 3 Linear Measurement Understanding length

### Math Focus Points

- Directly comparing two objects to determine which is longer

- Sorting objects into two categories according to length

- Developing language to describe and compare lengths (long, longer than, short, shorter than, the same, equal to)

When students count a tower of cubes to find out "how many," a natural question often arises: which tower has more—or which is longer—and how can we find out? Comparing is a natural way for students to approach measuring. Young children often spontaneously try to see who or what is bigger, taller, longer, or smaller. Therefore, the work in this unit focuses on introducing length and linear measurement through direct comparison. When students directly compare objects to determine which is longer, they have the opportunity to discuss and make sense of important aspects of accurate measurement, such as knowing which dimension to measure and how to line up objects to compare them. They also hear, become comfortable with, and use language to describe length—*long, short, wide, tall, high* (and the comparative forms, such as *longer, wider,* and so on). This kind of qualitative comparison lays the essential foundation that will help students develop accurate strategies for linear measurement over the course of the elementary school years.

## 4 Counting and Quantity Developing an understanding of the magnitude and position of numbers

### Math Focus Points

- Comparing two (or more) quantities to determine which is more

- Developing language for comparing quantities (more, greater, less, fewer, most, least, fewest, same, and equal to)

- Ordering quantities from least to most

Counting and understanding quantities involves understanding the relationships between and among numbers. As students are developing accurate counting strategies, they are also building an understanding of how the numbers in the counting sequence are related—each 1 more (or 1 less) than the number before (or after) it. In this unit, students compare quantities as they decide which Number Card shows more, which handful has more, which Inventory Bag holds more, or which name has more letters.

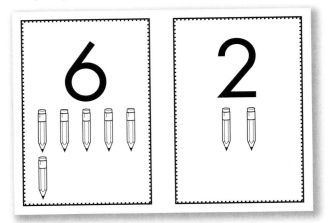

Through these activities, students develop an understanding of the concepts of *greater than, fewer than,* and *equal to* and develop language for describing quantitative comparisons (e.g., *bigger, more, smaller, fewer, less, same, equal*). This work with comparing two quantities lays the foundation for comparing and ordering more than two quantities (names, Number Cards, handfuls), which give students experience with concepts such as *biggest, greatest, most, smallest, fewest,* and *least.*

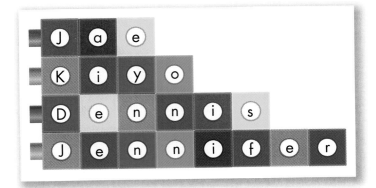

## 5 Whole Number Operations **Using manipulatives, drawings, tools, and notation to show strategies and solutions**

### Math Focus Points

◆ Representing quantities with pictures, numbers, objects, and/or words

◆ Using numerals to represent quantities

◆ Using a Ten-Frame to develop visual images of quantities up to 10

Throughout this unit and throughout the *Investigations* curriculum, students use mathematical tools and representations to model and solve problems and to clarify and communicate their thinking. For example, in this unit students are introduced to Ten-Frames as one way to visualize the numbers up to ten, and they use cubes to count and compare quantities.

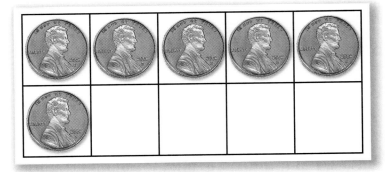

Although kindergarteners will vary widely in their ability to represent their mathematical work on paper, when they are asked to do so, they are encouraged to do so in ways that make sense to them. Many use some combination of pictures, words, and numbers.

## Classroom Routines focus on

- Developing strategies for counting accurately

- Considering whether order matters when you count

- Using the calendar as a tool for keeping track of time

- Collecting, counting, representing, describing, and comparing data

**LOOKING FORWARD**

The work in this unit is built upon in every unit in the Kindergarten sequence. In particular, in *Measuring and Counting* students build on the work they did with comparing lengths directly when they use craft sticks and cubes to measure lengths. This work and other activities provide further practice with counting and comparing. In *Measuring and Counting*, students also build on the foundation built in this unit as they order quantities, find the total after a small amount is added to (or taken away from) a set of objects, and figure out what they need to add to (or take away from) a set in order to make a set of a given size. Students also begin making sense of the operations of addition and subtraction as they act out stories and play games that involve combining or decomposing small quantities, and they develop a wide range of images for the quantities up to 10 by finding many different ways to arrange a set of square tiles.

# Assessment

Every session in this unit provides an opportunity for Ongoing Assessment. In addition, assessment checklists are provided to keep track of your observations about students' work with concepts and ideas that are benchmarks for this unit.

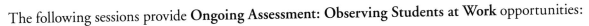

## ONGOING ASSESSMENT: Observing Students at Work

The following sessions provide **Ongoing Assessment: Observing Students at Work** opportunities:

- **Session 1.1, p. 30**
- **Session 1.2, p. 35**
- **Session 1.3, p. 41**
- **Session 1.4, p. 45**
- **Session 1.7, p. 58**
- **Session 1.9, p. 68**

- **Session 2.1, pp. 85–86**
- **Session 2.4, p. 97**
- **Session 2.5, pp. 102–103**
- **Session 2.6, p. 107**
- **Session 2.7, p. 114**

- **Session 2.8, p. 119**
- **Session 2.9, p. 124**
- **Session 2.10, p. 130**
- **Session 2.11, p. 136**
- **Session 2.12, p. 140**

## WRITING OPPORTUNITIES

The following sessions have **writing** opportunities for students to explain their mathematical thinking:

- **Session 1.2, p. 34**
  *Student Activity Book,* p. 5
- **Session 1.9, p. 67**
  *Student Activity Book,* p. 8
  M24, My Inventory Bag

- **Session 2.1, p. 84**
  *Student Activity Book,* p. 10
- **Session 2.9, p. 123**
  *Student Activity Book,* p. 12

- **Session 2.11, p. 135**
  *Student Activity Book,* p. 15

## PORTFOLIO OPPORTUNITIES

The following sessions have work appropriate for a **portfolio:**

- **Session 1.3, p. 41**
  Counting Jar
- **Session 1.4, p. 44**
  *Student Activity Book,* p. 6

- **Session 1.9, p. 68**
  *Student Activity Book,* p. 8
  M24, My Inventory Bag
- **Session 2.1, p. 84**
  *Student Activity Book,* p. 10

- **Session 2.9, p. 123**
  *Student Activity Book,* p. 12
- **Session 2.11, p. 135**
  *Student Activity Book,* p. 15

# Assessing the Benchmarks

Observing students as they engage in conversation about their ideas is a primary means to assess their mathematical understanding. Consider all of your students' work, not just the written assessments. See the chart below for suggestions about key activities to observe.

Assessment Checklists are introduced in Sessions 1.1, 2.1, and 2.4. Use these checklists to determine which students need to complete an End-of-Unit Assessment interview. Over the course of Sessions 2.13 and 2.14, meet individually with students who have not yet met each benchmark.

 Checklist Available

| Benchmarks in This Unit | Key Activities to Observe | Assessment |
|---|---|---|
| 1. Count a set of up to 10 objects. | Sessions 1.1–1.3, 1.5–1.8: Counting Books<br>Sessions 1.2–1.3, 1.5: *Grab and Count*<br>Sessions 1.3, 1.5–1.6, 1.8, 1.10, 2.1–2.3, 2.8–2.10: Counting Jar<br>Sessions 1.4–1.8, 1.10: Roll and Record<br>Sessions 1.7–1.8, 1.10: *Build It*<br>Sessions 1.9–1.10, 2.1–2.4: Inventory Bags | **Session 1.1 Assessment Checklist:**<br>Counting ✓ |
| 2. Decide which of two objects is longer. | Sessions 2.1–2.4: Measuring Table<br>Sessions 2.6–2.9: Longer/Shorter Hunt | **Session 2.1 Assessment Checklist:**<br>Comparing Lengths ✓ |
| 3. Compare two quantities up to 10 to see which is greater. | Sessions 2.4, 2.6–2.8: *Grab and Count: Compare*<br>Sessions 2.5–2.14: *Compare*<br>Sessions 2.9–2.10: Comparing Names | **Session 2.4 Assessment Checklist:**<br>Comparing Quantities ✓ |

# Relating the Mathematical Emphases to the Benchmarks

| Mathematical Emphases | Benchmarks |
|---|---|
| **Counting and Quantity** Developing strategies for accurately counting a set of objects by ones | 1 |
| **Counting and Quantity** Developing the idea of equivalence | |
| **Linear Measurement** Understanding length | 2 |
| **Counting and Quantity** Developing an understanding of the magnitude and position of numbers | 3 |
| **Whole Number Operations** Using manipulatives, drawings, tools, and notation to show strategies and solutions | |

# Algebra Connections

## IN THIS UNIT

In this unit, your students will have opportunities to engage with ideas that lay a foundation for algebra. Five-year-olds can and do think algebraically. Part of the work of Kindergarten is helping students learn to verbalize those thoughts, both as a way of engaging with generalizations about numbers and operations and as a foundation for meaningful use of algebraic notation in the future.

Many times over the course of a year, kindergarteners will work on the idea that a number describes the size of a set. The number of objects in a set is fixed no matter how it is arranged and counted, and different sets may have the same number of objects. Explorations of these issues offer opportunities for algebraic discussions. For example, consider the following vignette in which students are counting a set of red and yellow rods.

*Emma has arranged the rods, placing the five red rods in a row above the three yellow rods. Jason counts them and the class agrees that there are eight.*

**Teacher:** I noticed that when Jason counted, he counted the red ones first and the yellow ones second. Is there anybody who can count the yellow ones first and the red ones second? [The teacher rearranges the rods so that the reds are below the yellows. Mia volunteers to count them.]

**Teacher:** How many do you think she'll end up with if she starts with the yellow? [Many students say "the same thing."] The same thing? Carmen, why do you think she's going to end up with the same thing if we count them in a different order?

**Carmen:** Because you'll still have all the other ones unless you just take one away.

**Teacher:** Okay, we're still going to have all the other ones unless we take one away. Are we going to take one away? [Carmen responds "No."] No, what are we doing that's different?

**Carmen:** You're doing them in a different order.

**Teacher:** We're doing it in a different order. I have a really important question for you. Do you think it *matters* if we change the order? [Some students say "Yes," some say "No."] What will happen if we count the yellows first?

**Rebecca:** Nothing.

**Teacher:** Rebecca says, "Nothing." Nothing's going to happen; it's not going to change it. Rebecca, how come nothing will happen?

**Rebecca:** 'Cause it's eight still there.

**Teacher:** Okay, it's eight of them still.

**Mitchell:** Yeah. When you change it around and you have the yellow ones, it's still the same number.

**Teacher:** Okay, you say that when you change them around—tell me if I have this right—if you change it around, you have yellow ones still.

**Mitchell:** And it's still the same number.

**Teacher:** And it's still going to be the same number. Should we test it and see? [The class says yes. Mia touches each rod as she counts them, starting with the yellow and then counting the red rods.] What happened?

**Hugo:** Same number. . . . It's always going to be the same number.

**Teacher:** Is this getting the same number no matter what order you count something special about the rods, or would it work with anything?

**Emma:** If you take the same number, it would be the same.

**Teacher:** Do you think it's *always* going to be the same number? Even if we change the order around?

**Lionel:** It doesn't matter what number it is; it's still going to be the same number.

The students in this class are discussing whether order matters when counting. They explain that whether one counts the red rods first and then the yellow rods, or the yellow rods first and then the red rods, the total number of rods remains the same. While most of the discussion focuses on the eight rods laid out before them, Lionel generalizes to other numbers. He says, "It doesn't matter what number it is; it's still going to be the same number."

This idea—does order matter when counting?—will appear again in other forms throughout the grades. As students come to understand addition, the question will change to whether order matters when adding. Does changing the order of addends change the result? They will be able to rely on a similar image of red and yellow rods and know that the total number of rods is independent of the position of each set.

Years from now, students may represent their answer by using algebraic notation, $a + b = b + a$, and refer to it as the commutative property of addition. They may also ask similar questions about the other operations and conclude that addition and multiplication are commutative and that subtraction and division are not.

But most kindergarteners are not yet thinking in terms of operations; they are developing their understanding of numbers through counting. They are coming to recognize numbers as representing quantity; it describes the size of a set of objects independent of what those objects are. A set of eight fingers, eight pencils, eight children, and eight noses all share the attribute of "eightness."

Students will work on the question of order when counting in a variety of other contexts over the course of the year. For example, "When we counted the number of students in class today, and we started with Hugo, there were 24 children. How many children do you think there will be if we start with Rebecca? Why do you think so?" As students discuss such questions, they are developing a sense that the number of objects in a given set is fixed, no matter how they are counted.

The example presented illustrates the kind of "early algebraic reasoning" that is accessible to kindergarteners. This early algebra work involves students in reasoning, generalizing, representing, and communicating. They explore questions that may begin with a particular problem—does it matter whether we first count five red rods and then three yellow rods or first three yellow rods and then five red rods?—but extend to a whole class of problems. When counting a set of objects, it does not matter what order one counts them; the result is the same, no matter how many objects are in the set.

# Classroom Routines

**Classroom Routines** offer practice and review of key concepts for this grade level. These daily activities, to be done in 10 minutes outside of math class, occur in a regular rotation every 4–5 days. Specific directions for the day's routine are provided in each session. For the full description and variations of each classroom routine, see *Implementing Investigations in Kindergarten*.

## Attendance

Students count to determine the total number of students present. In order to help students connect the counting numbers to the quantities they represent, the class discusses how many students have counted midway through the count. They also explore what happens when the count begins with a different student.

### Math Focus Points

◈ Developing strategies for counting accurately

◈ Considering whether order matters when you count

## Calendar

Students review the numbers and counting sequence to 31 and the names and sequence of the days of the week. Students also use the calendar to determine how many days until (or since) a special event and explain their strategies.

### Math Focus Points

◈ Using the calendar as a tool for keeping track of time

◈ Developing strategies for counting accurately

## Today's Question

Students record on a two-column table their responses to a survey question with two possible answers. Class discussion focuses on describing and interpreting the data.

### Math Focus Points

◈ Collecting, counting, representing, describing, and comparing data

# Practice and Review

Practice and review play a critical role in the *Investigations* program. The following components and features are available to provide regular reinforcement of key mathematical concepts and procedures.

| Books | Features | In This Unit . . . |
|---|---|---|
| Curriculum Unit | **Classroom Routines** offer practice and review of key concepts for this grade level. These daily activities, to be done in ten minutes outside of math class, occur in a regular rotation every 4–5 days. Specific directions for the day's routine are provided in each session. For the full description and variations of each classroom routine see *Implementing Investigations in Kindergarten*. | • **All sessions** |
| Student Activity Book | **Practice** pages in the *Student Activity Book* provide one of two types of written practice: **reinforcement** of the content of the unit or **enrichment** opportunities. | • **Session 1.10** <br> • **Session 2.7** <br> • **Session 2.13** |
| | **Homework** pages in the *Student Activity Book* are an extension of the work done in class. At times they help students prepare for upcoming activities. | • **Session 2.10** |
| Student Math Handbook Flip Chart | **Math Words and Ideas** in the *Student Math Handbook Flip Chart* are pages that summarize key words and ideas. Most Words and Ideas pages have at least one exercise. | • **Student Math Handbook Flip Chart, pp. 4–10, 11–14, 17–24, 37** |

# Differentiation

## IN THIS UNIT

# Supporting the Range of Learners

| Sessions | 1.1 | 1.2 | 1.3 | 1.4 | 1.6 | 1.7 | 1.9 | 2.1 | 2.3 | 2.5 | 2.6 | 2.7 | 2.8 | 2.9 | 2.10 | 2.11 | 2.12 | 2.14 |
|---|---|---|---|---|---|---|---|---|---|---|---|---|---|---|---|---|---|---|
| Intervention | • | • |  | • |  | • |  | • |  | • |  | • | • | • | • | • | • |  |
| Extension | • | • | • | • | • |  | • |  | • |  | • | • |  | • |  | • |  | • |
| ELL | • |  |  |  |  |  | • | • |  |  |  |  |  | • |  |  |  |  |

## Intervention

Suggestions are made to support and engage students who are having difficulty with a particular idea, activity, or problem.

## Extension

Suggestions are made to support and engage students who finish early or may be ready for additional challenge.

## English Language Learners (ELL)

As English Language Learners work through the material in this unit, they need extensive exposure to the relevant vocabulary in the context of meaningful activities. In addition to learning the number names in English, they need to become familiar with common math-related terms, such as *first, last, how many, equal to,* and *most.* Present these words with visual examples as often as possible.

All students must develop their understanding of comparison as they work on this unit's activities. English Language Learners must also learn the terms commonly used for comparison, such as *same, different, smaller, more, less, fewer, least,* and so on.

To illustrate the meaning of the word *compare* and to introduce comparison vocabulary, you can show students two cubes towers that have the same number of cubes and later, two cube towers with different numbers of cubes.

Show the two towers with the same number of cubes side-by-side and say, Let's compare these two towers. They are the same. They have the same number of cubes. Encourage students to repeat *same* after you. Then show students two towers with different numbers of cubes and say, Let's compare these two towers. Are they the same? No, they are not the same. This tower has *more* than that tower. This tower has *fewer* than that tower. Encourage students to practice with other cube towers.

*Working with the Range of Learners: Classroom Cases* is a set of episodes written by teachers that focuses on meeting the needs of the range of learners in the classroom. In the first section, *Setting up the Mathematical Community,* teachers write about how they create a supportive and productive learning environment in their classrooms. In the next section, *Accommodations for Learning,* teachers focus on specific modifications they make to meet the needs of some of their learners. In the last section, *Language and Representation,* teachers share how they help students use representations and develop language to investigate and express mathematical ideas. The questions at the end of each case provide a starting point for your own reflection or for discussion with colleagues. See *Implementing Investigations in Kindergarten* for this set of episodes.

## Mathematical Emphases

**Counting and Quantity** Developing strategies for accurately counting a set of objects by ones

### Math Focus Points

◆ Developing strategies for accurately counting and keeping track of quantities up to 12

◆ Connecting number words, numerals, and quantities

◆ Developing visual images for quantities up to 6

**Counting and Quantity** Developing the idea of equivalence

### Math Focus Points

◆ Creating an equivalent set

◆ Considering whether order matters when you count

**Whole Number Operations** Using manipulatives, drawings, tools, and notation to show strategies and solutions

### Math Focus Points

◆ Representing quantities with pictures, numbers, objects, and/or words

◆ Using numerals to represent quantities

◆ Using a Ten-Frame to develop visual images of quantities up to 10

# Counting

| | Student Activity Book | Student Math Handbook | Professional Development: Read Ahead of Time | |
|---|---|---|---|---|
| **SESSION 1.1**      p. 26 | | | | |
| **A Counting Book** The class reads a counting book. After examining how the book is structured, students begin to make their own counting books, with one page for each number, 1 through 6. | | 4–10 | • **Mathematics in This Unit**, p. 10<br>• **Dialogue Boxes:** What Do We Count and Why?, p. 163; Pictures in a Counting Book, p. 164<br>• **Teacher Notes:** Counting Is More Than 1, 2, 3, p. 151; Observing Kindergarteners as They Count, p. 152; Assessing Students' Counting, p. 153; Students' Counting Books, p. 157 | |
| **SESSION 1.2**      p. 33 | | | | |
| **Grab and Count** Students are introduced to *Grab and Count,* an activity in which they grab a handful of objects, figure out how many they grabbed, and find a way to record their handful. Math Workshop focuses on counting and connecting the number words to the written numbers and to the quantities they represent. | 5 | 19 | • **Part 2: How to Use** *Investigations* in *Implementing Investigations in Kindergarten:* Components of the Program | |
| **SESSION 1.3**      p. 39 | | | | |
| **Counting Jar** Students revisit the Counting Jar. In this version, two distinct groups (e.g., 5 red, 3 blue) are placed in the jar. Math Workshop continues to focus on counting and on making connections between number words, numerals, and quantities. | | 20 | | |
| **SESSION 1.4**      p. 43 | | | | |
| **Roll and Record** Students learn, play, and discuss *Roll and Record,* a game in which players roll a 1–6 dot cube, determine the number rolled, and record that number on a recording sheet. | 6 | 4–10, 11–14 | | |
| **SESSION 1.5**      p. 47 | | | | |
| **How Did I Count?** Math Workshop continues to focus on counting and on making connections between number words, numerals, and quantities. Class discussion focuses on common counting errors. | | 19 | | |

# Classroom Routines See page 18 for an overview.

| *Calendar* | *Attendance* |
|---|---|
| • Monthly calendar | • No materials needed |

*Today's Question*
- Charts for Sessions 1.3, 1.6, and 1.9. See instructions on pages 39, 51, and 65.

| Materials to Gather | Materials to Prepare |
|---|---|
| • **A counting book (in big book form, if possible)** Examples include: *Anno's Counting Book* by Mitsumasa Anno, *How Many, How Many, How Many* by Rick Walton, *Ten Black Dots* by Donald Crews, *Feast for 10* by Cathryn Falwell, or *Count and See* by Tana Hoban.<br>• **Art supplies** | • **M3, Assessment Checklist: Counting** ☑ Make copies. (3–4 per class)<br>• **M1–M2, Family Letter** Make copies. (1 per student)<br>• **Chart paper** Title a piece of chart paper "About Our Counting Book."<br>• **M4–M11, Counting Book** Make copies. Collate pages and staple together to make booklets. (1 per student) |
| • **Materials for Making a Counting Book** See Session 1.1. | • **M13–M18, Counting Book** Make copies. (as needed) Collate pages and add to students' Counting Book. (1 per student)<br>• **Bins of items** Each bin should contain only one kind of item, such as connecting cubes, color tiles, teddy bear counters, or foam peanuts. Items should be small enough to allow for student handfuls of 5–12 items. |
| • **Materials for Counting Jar** (as you have set it up)<br>• **Materials for Making a Counting Book** See Session 1.1.<br>• **Materials for *Grab and Count*** See Session 1.2.<br>• **Bins of smaller items** (such as marker caps, or buttons for the variation) | • **M12, *Grab and Count*** Make copies. (as needed)<br>• **Counting Jar** Place 5 red tiles and 3 blue tiles in the jar. |
| • **Dot cubes** (1 per student) | • **M19, *Roll and Record* Recording Sheet** Make copies. (as needed) |
| • **Connecting cubes** (1 bin)<br>• **Materials for *Roll and Record*** See session 1.4.<br>• **Materials for Counting Jar** See Session 1.3.<br>• **Materials for *Grab and Count*** See Session 1.2.<br>• **Materials for Making a Counting Book** See Session 1.1. | |

☑ Checklist Available

# Counting, *continued*

| SESSION 1.6　　　　　p. 51 | Student Activity Book | Student Math Handbook | Professional Development: Read Ahead of Time | |
|---|---|---|---|---|
| **Does Order Matter When You Count?** Math Workshop continues to focus on counting and on making connections between number words, numerals, and quantities. Class discussion focuses on whether order matters when you count. | | 17 | • **Algebra Connections in This Unit**, p. 16<br>• **Dialogue Box:** Does the Order Matter?, p. 165 | |
| **SESSION 1.7　　　　　p. 55** | | | | |
| **Build It** Students are introduced to *Build It*, a game that involves creating a set to match a given number. Math Workshop focuses on counting and on connecting number words, numerals, and quantities. | 7 | 11–14 | | |
| **SESSION 1.8　　　　　p. 61** | | | | |
| **Counting Jar** The Counting Jar, with 10 objects in it, is added to Math Workshop. The session ends with a discussion focused on students' Counting Books. | | 20 | | |
| **SESSION 1.9　　　　　p. 65** | | | | |
| **Inventories** The class discusses "taking inventory" as a reason for counting things. Students inventory the contents of a bag and make a representation to show their results. Class discussion focuses on strategies for recording. | 8 | 17, 18, 19 | | |
| **SESSION 1.10　　　　p. 71** | | | | |
| **Strategies for Accurate Counting** Math Workshop continues. The session ends with a discussion about counting, focused on what happens when different students (or pairs) count the same set and get different numbers. | 9 | | • **Dialogue Box:** Is It 10 or 11?, p. 167 | |

| Materials to Gather | Materials to Prepare |
|---|---|
| • Materials for *Roll and Record*  See Session 1.4.<br>• Materials for Counting Jar  See Session 1.3.<br>• Materials for Making a Counting Book  See Session 1.1.<br>• Counting Jar (from Session 1.3)<br>• The Counting Jar Poster or Counting Jar Booklets (from Unit 1) | |
| • Counters (10 per student)<br>• Materials for *Roll and Record*  See Session 1.4.<br>• Materials for Making a Counting Book  See Session 1.1. | • M20–M23, Primary Number Cards  If you're not using the manufactured cards, make copies on cardstock or heavy paper. Laminate if possible. Cut out. (1 set of cards per student) |
| • Materials for Counting Jar routine (as you have set it up)<br>• Materials for *Build It*  See Session 1.7.<br>• Materials for *Roll and Record*  See Session 1.4.<br>• Materials for Making a Counting Book  See Session 1.1. | • Counting Jar  Place 10 pennies (or other objects) in the jar. |
| • Art supplies | • M3, Assessment Checklist: Counting ☑ (as needed)<br>• Inventory Bags  Fill small bags with 5–12 identical or similar classroom items. The number in the bags will depend on how high your students are counting comfortably. Place a different kind of item in each bag. Label each bag with a letter and the name of the items inside. Possible items include erasers, unsharpened pencils, buttons, paper clips, rulers, crayons, markers, cubes, tiles, teddy bear counters, pattern blocks, and thread spools. (1 per pair, plus a few extras)<br>• M24, My Inventory Bag  Make copies. (as needed) |
| • Materials for Inventory Bags  See Session 1.9.<br>• Counting Jar (from Session 1.8)<br>• Materials for Counting Jar  See Session 1.8.<br>• Materials for *Build It*  See Session 1.7.<br>• Materials for *Roll and Record*  See Session 1.4. | |

☑ Checklist Available

# A Counting Book

## Math Focus Points

- Developing strategies for accurately counting and keeping track of quantities up to 6
- Connecting number words, numerals, and quantities
- Creating equivalent sets
- Representing quantities with pictures and/or numbers

### Vocabulary

**count**
**zero**

| Today's Plan | | | Materials |
|---|---|---|---|
| **ACTIVITY** ❶ **A Counting Book** | 🕐 10 MIN | 👥 CLASS | • A counting book, in big book form, if possible |
| **ACTIVITY** ❷ **Introducing Counting Books** | 🕐 10 MIN | 👥 CLASS | • M4–M11* <br> • Chart: "About Our Counting Book"* |
| **ACTIVITY** ❸ **Making a Counting Book** | 🕐 10–20 MIN | 👤 INDIVIDUALS | • M3 ☑ * <br> • M4–M11 (1 set per student)* <br> • Art supplies |
| **DISCUSSION** ❹ **Checking In** | 🕐 5 MIN | 👥 CLASS | |
| **SESSION FOLLOW-UP** ❺ **Practice and Homework** | | | • *Student Math Handbook,* pp. 4–10 <br> • M1–M2, Family Letter* |

*See *Materials to Prepare,* p. 23.

## Classroom Routines

*Calendar: Days of the Week* Use the calendar to review the days of the week, noting which days are school days and which are weekend (or nonschool) days.

**ACTIVITY**

# A Counting Book

⏱ 10 MIN  👥 CLASS

We're going to read a counting book today. Who has an idea about what it means to count? Can you think about some times when we count in our class?

**Students might say:**

"We count when we take attendance."

"We count to make sure each snack is fair."

Ask students to think about what they are counting at these times and why. ❶

The book we're going to read today is called *[Anno's Counting Book]*. What do you think this book is about? What do you notice about the cover? Does it give you any clues?

After students share a few ideas, ask what they think might be on the first page.

If this is a counting book, what might be on the first page? Why do you think so?

After hearing students' ideas, turn to the first page. If your book starts with zero, have a discussion about what this number means and what it represents.

Zero is another number, just like 1, 2, and 3. How many of you have ever heard of zero? Does anyone know what a zero means? ❸

If the book begins with the number one, ask this question:

Is this what you expected? What do you notice about this page? Do you see just one of anything on this page?

Read the book together and encourage students to comment on what they notice and to find groups of things that match the number on the page. Occasionally ask students what number they think will be next. ❷ ❹

---

**Professional Development**

❶ **Dialogue Box:** What Do We Count and Why?, p. 163

❷ **Dialogue Box:** Pictures in a Counting Book, p. 164

**Math Note**

❸ **Zero** Students may be surprised by a counting book that starts with 0. Some think it is the letter O or a circle. Others know there is nothing on the page but are unsure how the written number corresponds with that fact. Still others say that zero means "nothing;" for example, "If I have zero apples, I don't have any at all."

**Teaching Note**

❹ **Revisiting Pages, Revisiting Stories** Many counting books have many layers and much detail. Therefore, students often notice new elements as you read (and each time you read) and want to find out whether those elements appeared on earlier pages. Investigate such things as students notice them.

_____'s

**Counting
Book**

M4  Unit 2                    Sessions 1.1, 1.2, 1.3, 1.5, 1.6, 1.7, 1.8

▲ **Resource Masters, M4–M11**

10 MIN    CLASS

### ACTIVITY

# Introducing Counting Books

Ask students about the structure of the counting book you read as a whole class.

*If we wanted to make a counting book like this one, what sorts of things would we need to include on each page? What does every page in this book have?*

Hold the book open and flip through the pages as students think about these questions. When an idea is suggested, flip through the book to look for illustrations of that idea.

**Students might say:**

"There's a number on every page."

*Let's see . . . does this page have a number? Does this one?*

To encourage students to listen to one another, ask them to think of characteristics of the book that someone else has not already shared. Use simple words and sketches to record students' ideas on chart paper. Consider these suggestions made by a class after reading *Anno's Counting Book*.

**Students might say:**

"On every page, there are more and more things."

"Each page goes up one number: 1, 2, 3 . . ."

 "Every page has a number that matches the number of things in the picture."

 "Every page shows the numbers with cubes."

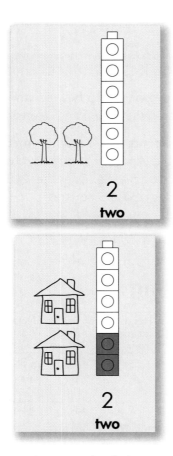

Explain that students are going to make their own counting books over the next few sessions for the numbers 1 through 6. Show them the blank counting books you have prepared (M4–M11) and the line for them to write their names. Explain that they can draw and color their illustrations, but they can also use stamps, stickers, stencils, and items cut out of magazines or catalogs to illustrate the pages.

## Teaching Note

⑤ **Assessing Students' Counting** By the end of this unit, students are expected to be able to count a set of 10 objects accurately (Benchmark 1). This means that they know the number names in sequence, say one number for each object, and have a system for keeping track of what they are counting. Use Assessment Checklist: Counting (M3) to keep track of your observations about students' counting skills over the course of this Investigation and unit.

## Professional Development

⑥ **Teacher Notes:** Counting Is More Than 1, 2, 3, p. 151; Observing Kindergarteners as They Count, p. 152; Assessing Students' Counting, p. 153; Students' Counting Books, p. 157

## Math Note

⑦ **What's the Math?** Keep in mind that creating a set of a given size (e.g., "Can you make a group of six?") is a different task from counting a given set (e.g., "Here are some cubes. How many are there?").

As you talk about what their books might look like, remind students of things they noticed about the counting book you read together. Keep in mind that it is unlikely that students will stay with a single theme throughout their book; for example, one flower on page one may be followed by two people on page two.

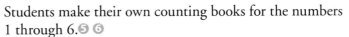

**ACTIVITY**

# 3 Making a Counting Book

10–20 MIN  INDIVIDUALS

Students make their own counting books for the numbers 1 through 6.⑤ ⑥

**ONGOING ASSESSMENT: Observing Students at Work**

Students make connections between the number names, numerals, and quantities as they count and create sets of a given size.⑦

- **How do students figure out how many items to draw on each page?** Do they know what quantity a written number represents? Is their work accurate (e.g., Does the "2" page have groups of 2 things on it? Do they color in 2 squares?)

# Assessment Checklist: Counting

| Student | Knows the names of the numbers in order | Counts each object once and only once | Has a system for keeping track | Double-checks | Notes Additional math: creates sets with the right amount |
|---|---|---|---|---|---|
| Tammy 9/27 | ✓ to 6 | ✓ | Looks like no, but ✓ | | Looks messy, incorrect, but many groups of the right #. |
| Hugo 9/27 | ✓ to 6 | ✓ | ✓ | | Errors seem more about structure of Anno book, the zero page, than counting. |
| Corey 9/27 | ✓ to 6 | ✓ | ✓ | ✓ | Struggle to fix 6 page - must x out 2 (rather than add more to make 2 grps of 6) |
| Mitchell 9/27 | ✓ to 6 | Tenuous → | | | |
| Jennifer 9/28 | ✓ to 6 | ✓ | ✓ | | Counts set of 6 well, but when asked how many she recounts. |

- **How accurate are students as they count?** Do they know the sequence? Do they say one number for each object? Do they count each object once and only once? Do they double-check?

- **How do students keep track while they are drawing?** For example, while drawing five people, what do they do after they have drawn the third? Do they recount from 1 to see how many they have? Do they know they have 3 and go on to 4? Do they know that they need two more?

## DIFFERENTIATION: Supporting the Range of Learners

**Intervention** Some students are more comfortable counting objects they can manipulate, such as blocks, rather than groups that are static, such as pictures that cannot be moved around or picked up. Encourage them to place one cube or counter on each picture, count the cubes and then remove the cubes and count the pictures. Encourage students who are spending a great deal of time on detailed drawings to think about quicker ways to show objects such as using rubber stamps, stencils, stickers, or pictures cut out of magazines or catalogs. Such materials are also good for students who are not comfortable with drawing.

**Extension** Encourage students who quickly draw one group on each page and announce that they have finished to add more groups to the pages.

**ELL** If some English Language Learners do not yet know the number names in English, work one-on-one or with a small group. Use different classroom objects, such as crayons, counters, or other math manipulatives, to practice counting in English until each student is able to repeat the numbers without your help. Repeat the word "count" frequently (e.g., "Let's **count** these crayons . . . 1, 2, 3.") to reinforce the word and its meaning.

## DISCUSSION

**5 MIN    CLASS**

# ④ Checking In

Take this opportunity to discuss any difficulties that you noticed while observing students at work. The topics may be mathematical in nature, such as a strategy you would like all students to consider—for example, how a student showed many examples of a quantity on one page—or a common error you would like students to discuss, for example, what happens when you count your pictures and they do not match the number on the page?

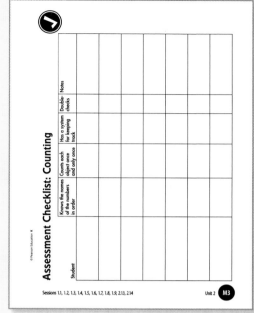

**Assessment Checklist: Counting**

| Student | Knows the names of the numbers in order | Counts each object once and only once | Has a system for keeping track | Double-checks | Notes |
|---|---|---|---|---|---|

Sessions 1.1, 1.2, 1.3, 1.4, 1.5, 1.6, 1.7, 1.8, 1.9, 2.13, 2.14          Unit 2  **M3**

 ▲ **Resource Masters, M3** ✔

The difficulty may be logistical, such as sharing strategies for gluing down pictures or for adding more examples on each page without doing detailed drawings, or management-related—working independently, managing and cleaning up art supplies, working productively.

Other alternatives include checking in with students about how far they have progressed (e.g., "Thumbs up if you worked on the 1 page. Thumbs up if you worked on the 2 page."), asking everyone to hold up their work for a particular page, or allowing students to raise questions or make comments about today's math class.

End by reassuring students that they will have plenty of time to work on their counting books over the next few sessions, and explain where they should put their books so that they can find them when they are ready to work on them again.

### SESSION FOLLOW-UP
# Practice and Homework

 **Student Math Handbook Flip Chart:** Use the *Student Math Handbook Flip Chart* pages 4–10 to reinforce concepts from today's session. See pages 176–181 in the back of this unit.

 **Family Letter:** Have each student take home a copy of Family Letter (M1–M2).

# Grab and Count

## Math Focus Points

◆ Developing strategies for accurately counting and keeping track of quantities up to 12

◆ Representing quantities up to 12 with pictures, numbers, and/or words

◆ Creating equivalent sets

## Vocabulary

**handful**

| Today's Plan | | Materials |
|---|---|---|
| **ACTIVITY**<br>**① Introducing *Grab and Count***<br><br>5–10 MIN CLASS | | • *Student Activity Book*, p. 5<br>• Bins of items (such as connecting cubes, color tiles, teddy bear counters, or foam peanuts) that result in student handfuls of 5–12* |
| **MATH WORKSHOP**<br>**② Representing Quantities**<br>**②A** *Grab and Count*<br>**②B** Making a Counting Book<br><br>20–30 MIN | | **②A** • Materials from Activity 1<br>  • *Student Activity Book*, p. 5<br>**②B** • Materials from Session 1.1, p. 26<br>  • M13–M18* |
| **DISCUSSION**<br>**③ Checking In**<br><br>5 MIN CLASS | | |
| **SESSION FOLLOW-UP**<br>**④ Practice** | | • *Student Math Handbook Flip Chart*, p. 19 |

*See *Materials to Prepare*, p. 23.

## Classroom Routines

*Attendance: How Many Have Counted?* Count around the circle to determine the total number of students present. Pause several times during the count to ask students how many people have counted so far. Help students see why the number they say represents the number of students who have counted so far and that the last number represents the total number of students in class today.

## Teaching Note

**❶ Why Five?** In order to make an estimate, students need to have a sense of quantity. Consistently showing students 5 as a referent quantity helps them get a really good sense of 5—what it looks like and how to count it. It also encourages students to make estimates and adjust them on the basis of known information.

▲ **Student Activity Book, p. 5; Resource Masters, M12**

**ACTIVITY**

 **Introducing *Grab and Count***

5–10 MIN   CLASS

Introduce this game by asking what it means to grab a handful of something. After students have shared their ideas, show them a container with objects, such as the cubes, for which "a handful" will be a fairly small quantity.

Count out five of that item and set these out for students to use as a reference in estimating quantities.❶

This pile has five [objects]. How many [objects] do you think [Kiyo] can grab in one **handful**?

Collect some estimates, and then ask your volunteer to grab a handful of cubes from the container and place them where everyone can see them.

About how many [objects] do you think there are in [Kiyo]'s handful? Does it look like five? More than five? Fewer than five?

If the handful had more than five, count out five and ask students whether the amount left has more (or fewer) than five.

As a class, count all of the items in the handful by 1s. You may also have several volunteers model how they would count them.

Then, introduce *Student Activity Book* page 5.

What if we wanted to show [Kiyo's] handful on this paper? What could we do so that someone looking at her paper could tell what she grabbed?

### Students might say:

 "We could draw a picture of the cubes."

Collect a few suggestions, but know that students often develop ideas as they actually do the activity. Explain that this game will be one of two activities that students can choose during Math Workshop.

**MATH WORKSHOP**

# Representing Quantities

 20–30 MIN INDIVIDUALS

**Professional Development**

 **Teacher Note: Part 2: How to Use** *Investigations* in *Implementing Investigations in Kindergarten:* Components of the Program

Explain that the following two activities are available during this Math Workshop. Remind students what each activity entails, the materials that are required, and where they are located.

Point out the different bins of *Grab and Count* materials so that students know that they are expected to do this activity with these objects over the course of the next few days.

You may also show a few of the Counting Books begun in Session 1.1, and refer students to the poster you created together in Session 1.1. Challenge students to create a book that has more than one group on each page.

## 2A Grab and Count

 INDIVIDUALS

Students grab a handful of items, count them, and find a way to record what they grabbed on *Student Activity Book* page 5.

### ONGOING ASSESSMENT: Observing Students at Work

Students practice counting and representing a set of objects.

- **How do students count their handfuls?** Do they count accurately, counting each item once and only once? Do they double-check?

- **Do students count the items in a random configuration, or do they organize them in some way?** Do they touch or move each item as they count it?

- **How do students represent their handfuls?** Do they draw each item? Do they use numbers or the name of the item? Do they use groups or tallies?

### DIFFERENTIATION: Supporting the Range of Learners

**Intervention** For some students, representing information on paper may be a difficult and frustrating task. Suggest that they use stamps or stickers to show their handfuls. Take dictation from students who are struggling to represent their work.

## 2B Making a Counting Book

**INDIVIDUALS**

For complete details about this activity, see Session 1.1, pages 28–31.

*Sample Student Work*

*Sample Student Work*

## DIFFERENTIATION: Supporting the Range of Learners

 **Extension** Some students may want to extend their counting books to show larger numbers. They can do this by adding some or all of Counting Book (M13–M18) to their books.

*Sample Student Work*

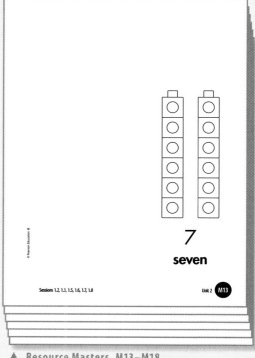

▲ **Resource Masters, M13–M18**

---

**DISCUSSION**

## 3 Checking In

**5 MIN  CLASS**

Take this opportunity to discuss any difficulties that you noticed while observing students at work. The topic may be mathematical in nature, such as a strategy you would like all students to consider—keeping track of a count by moving each object as it is counted, or a common error or misconception you would like students to discuss—skipping or double counting objects, or omitting or repeating numbers, while counting.

The difficulty may also be logistical—getting materials out and putting them away, or management related—grabbing a reasonably-sized handful rather than trying to grab as many as possible or working productively during Math Workshop.

Other alternatives include checking in with students about which activities they have been choosing (e.g., "Thumbs up if you worked on your Counting Book today. Thumbs up if you worked on *Grab and Count*."), asking everyone to hold up a *Grab and Count* Recording Sheet, or allowing students to raise a question or make a comment about today's math class.

**SESSION FOLLOW-UP**

# Practice

**Student Math Handbook Flip Chart:** Use the *Student Math Handbook Flip Chart* page 19 to reinforce concepts from today's session. See pages 176–181 in the back of this unit.

# Counting Jar

## Math Focus Points

◆ Developing strategies for accurately counting and keeping track of quantities up to 12

◆ Creating an equivalent set

◆ Representing quantities with pictures, numbers, and/or words

| Today's Plan | | | Materials |
|---|---|---|---|
| **ACTIVITY**<br>**① Introducing the Counting Jar** | ⏱<br>5–10 MIN | 👥<br>CLASS | • Counting Jar* |
| **MATH WORKSHOP**<br>**② Counting and Representing Quantities**<br>**2A** Counting Jar<br>**2B** *Grab and Count*<br>**2C** Making a Counting Book | ⏱<br>20–30 MIN | | **2A** • Counting Jar* from Activity 1<br>• Materials for the Counting Jar (as you have it set up)<br>**2B** • M12*<br>• Materials from Session 1.2, p. 33; bins of smaller items<br>**2C** • Materials from Session 1.1, p. 26 |
| **DISCUSSION**<br>**③ Checking In** | ⏱<br>5 MIN | 👥<br>CLASS | |
| **SESSION FOLLOW-UP**<br>**④ Practice** | | | • *Student Math Handbook Flip Chart*, p. 20 |

*See *Materials to Prepare*, p. 23.

## Classroom Routines

*Today's Question: Are you a boy or a girl?* On chart paper, create a vertical two-column table entitled "Are you a boy or a girl?" with the label "Boy" at the bottom of one column and "Girl" at the botttom of the other. Have students write their names above the appropriate label. Count the responses as a class. After counting, have a short discussion about the results of the survey.

ACTIVITY

5–10 MIN  CLASS

# 1 Introducing the Counting Jar

Place five red and three blue square tiles in the Counting Jar and show it to students. Because the Counting Jar should be a familiar activity by this point in the school year, students should need only a brief review of how this activity works in your classroom.

I've put a set of objects in the Counting Jar. Your job is to visit the jar at some point over the next few days and find out how many objects are in it. Then make a set of your own that has the same number of objects, and record what you found out.

Take a minute to discuss strategies for figuring out how to write a number.

Suppose I counted and I thought there were six things in the jar, but I didn't know how to write a six. How could I figure out what a six looks like?

**Students might say:**

"I could look at the calendar and find a six."

As you discuss students' ideas, be sure to point out other places in your classroom—the class number line, the 100 Chart, the number line at the bottom of the Counting Jar poster—where students can find the written numbers in order. Model, or have students model, counting on one or more of these tools from 1 to 6. ❶

MATH WORKSHOP

20–30 MIN  INDIVIDUALS

# 2 Counting and Representing Quantities

Explain that the following three activities are available during this Math Workshop. Remind students what each activity entails, what materials are required, and where they are located.

## 2A Counting Jar

**INDIVIDUALS**

Students count the objects in the Counting Jar—a set of five red and three blue square tiles. They make a set of the same size and then find a way to record what they found out.

### ONGOING ASSESSMENT: Observing Students at Work

Students count a set of objects, create an equivalent set, and record their work.

- **How do students count the objects in the jar?** Do they organize the objects in any way? Do they know the sequence of number names? Do they count each item once and only once? Do they double-check?

- **Do any students use the two subsets to figure out the number in the jar (e.g., "5 and 3 more is 5, 6, 7, 8")?**

- **How do students create an equivalent set?** Do they think, "The Counting Jar has eight. I need eight tiles. One, two, three . . . "? Do they recreate the Counting Jar set, matching them one to one? Do they double-check?

- **How do students record their work?** Do they draw a picture of the items?

As you observe, look for students who sort the tiles into lines of each color to count them. You will refer to this strategy during the discussion at the end of Session 1.6.

## 2B Grab and Count

**INDIVIDUALS**

For complete details on this activity, see Session 1.2, page 34.

### DIFFERENTIATION: Supporting the Range of Learners

**Extension** Students who are ready to count slightly larger quantities can grab and count materials that result in larger handfuls such as marker caps, rocks, or buttons.

## 2C Making a Counting Book

**INDIVIDUALS**

For complete details on this activity, see Session 1.1, page 28.

**Teaching Note**

❷ **Assembling a Portfolio** Because students do Counting Jar in every unit, you will have an opportunity to see students' growth over time. Therefore, have students record their work on a piece of paper you can later collect and put in their portfolio.

**5 MIN    CLASS**

### DISCUSSION
# ③ Checking In

Take this opportunity to discuss any difficulties that you noticed while observing students at work. The topic may be mathematical in nature, such as a strategy you would like all students to consider, such as lining up objects to count them; or a common error or misconception that you would like students to discuss, such as counting the number of red tiles and the number of blue tiles in the Counting Jar but not finding the total number of tiles.

The difficulty may also be logistical, such as reminding students of the steps involved in the Counting Jar activity; or management-related, such as noise level, making choices, and working productively during Math Workshop.

Other alternatives include checking in with students about which activities they have been choosing (e.g., "Thumbs up if you worked on your Counting Book today. Thumbs up if you worked on *Grab and Count.* Thumbs up if you visited the Counting Jar."), or asking about students' progress with a particular activity (e.g., "Thumbs up if you've worked on the Four page, the Five page, etc. Raise your hand if you think your Counting Book is finished.").

### SESSION FOLLOW-UP
# ④ Practice

**Student Math Handbook Flip Chart:** Use the *Student Math Handbook Flip Chart* page 20 to reinforce concepts from today's session. See pages 176–181 in the back of this unit.

# Roll and Record

## Math Focus Points

◆ Developing visual images for quantities up to 6

◆ Connecting number words, numerals, and quantities

◆ Using numerals to represent quantities

| Today's Plan | | | Materials |
|---|---|---|---|
| **ACTIVITY** ① **Introducing** *Roll and Record* | 🕐 5–10 MIN | 👥 CLASS | • *Student Activity Book*, p. 6 <br> • Dot cube |
| **ACTIVITY** ② **Playing** *Roll and Record* | 🕐 20–30 MIN | 👥 INDIVIDUALS | • *Student Activity Book*, p. 6 <br> • M19* <br> • Dot cubes |
| **DISCUSSION** ③ **Checking In** | 🕐 5 MIN | 👥 CLASS | |
| **SESSION FOLLOW-UP** ④ **Practice** | | | • *Student Math Handbook Flip Chart*, pp. 4–10, 11–14 |

*See *Materials to Prepare,* p. 23.

## Classroom Routines

*Calendar: How Many Days . . . ?* Students use the calendar to determine how many days until a class event or holiday that will happen this month. Discuss students' strategies for determining the number of days.

## Teaching Notes

**① What Number Do I Write?** The "How Many?" pages of your *Student Math Handbook Flip Chart* include dot images. These pages, and the Number pages 0–10, can also help students to determine what number they should record.

**② Modeling Number Formation** Teach students how to form the numbers during the handwriting portion of your curriculum. Use the strategies presented there when you use numbers to record for the class.

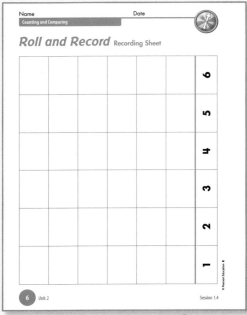

▲ Student Activity Book, p. 6; Resource Masters, M19

### ACTIVITY
# ① Introducing *Roll and Record*

5–10 MIN   CLASS

Before introducing *Roll and Record,* show students the dot cube they will be using as they play. Pass several around and ask students what they notice. Then, explain the game by playing a demonstration game with the class.

Today we are going to play a game called *Roll and Record.* You need a dot cube and a recording sheet to play this game.

The first thing you do is roll the dot cube. [Roll the cube.] How many dots do you see? [Three.] We agree that I rolled a [three.] So now I write a [3] in the [3] column [pointing to the 3 column on *Student Activity Book* page 6]. What if I don't know what a 3 looks like? How can I figure out how to write a 3?

Collect students' ideas, being sure to discuss how to use the numbers at the bottom of the *Student Activity Book* page to count up to the number rolled.① Model how to record your roll.②

So I rolled a 3, and we counted 1, 2, 3 to find the 3 on my recording sheet. Now I am going to write a 3 in the column.

Play several more rounds, asking volunteers to roll the dot cube, to count the dots, and to tell you what number you should record in which column. Play enough rounds so that students see what happens when you roll a number more than once. Explain that the game is over when there is a number written in every box in one column.

*The teacher models how to record the number rolled.*

## Teaching Note

❸ **Assembling a Portfolio** Students will play several variations of *Roll and Record* during the year. Placing a recording sheet in their portfolio will provide a picture of students' growth in writing the numbers over the course of the year.

## ② ACTIVITY
# Playing *Roll and Record*

**20–30 MIN   INDIVIDUALS**

Students roll a dot cube and record the number rolled on *Student Activity Book* page 6.❸

## ONGOING ASSESSMENT: Observing Students at Work

Students count, become familiar with dot arrangements, and practice writing the numbers from 1 to 6.

- **How do students figure out what they roll?** Do they count the dots? Do they "just know" the dot pattern?

- **Can students write the numbers accurately?** Do they use available tools to figure out how to write a number they do not know?

## DIFFERENTIATION: Supporting the Range of Learners

**Intervention** If students are having difficulty accurately forming the numbers, make this a focus of your handwriting curriculum.

**Extension** Students often become very interested in which number "wins." Although the goal of this game is connecting numbers and quantities, you can ask students questions about their completed game sheet, such as, "Which number did you roll the most times?" and "How many times did you roll a 3?"

## DISCUSSION

# 3 Checking In

**5 MIN    CLASS**

Take this opportunity to discuss any difficulties that you noticed while observing students at work. The topic may be mathematical in nature, such as a strategy you would like all students to consider (e.g., using the number line to figure out how to write a number) or a common error you would like students to discuss (e.g., reversals).

The issue might be logistical (e.g., clarifying the rules of the game) or management-related (e.g., noise level, working independently, sharing a dot cube).

You may also ask everyone to share what they did by holding up a completed recording sheet.

## SESSION FOLLOW-UP

# 4 Practice

**Student Math Handbook Flip Chart:** Use the *Student Math Handbook Flip Chart* pages 4–10, 11–14 to reinforce concepts from today's session. See pages 176–181 in the back of this unit.

# How Did I Count?

## Math Focus Points

- Developing strategies for accurately counting and keeping track of quantities up to 12
- Connecting number words, numerals, and quantities
- Representing quantities with pictures, numbers, and/or words

| Today's Plan | | Materials |
|---|---|---|
| **MATH WORKSHOP** **① Using Pictures and Numbers to Represent Quantities** **1A** *Roll and Record* **1B** Counting Jar **1C** *Grab and Count* **1D** Making a Counting Book | 20–35 MIN | **1A** • Materials from Session 1.4, p. 43 **1B** • Materials from Session 1.3, p. 39 **1C** • Materials from Session 1.2, p. 33 **1D** • Materials from Session 1.1, p. 26 |
| **DISCUSSION** **② How Did I Count?** | 10 MIN   CLASS | • Connecting cubes (1 bin) |
| **SESSION FOLLOW-UP** **③ Practice** | | • *Student Math Handbook Flip Chart*, p. 19 |

## Classroom Routines

*Attendance: What If We Start With . . . ?*  Count around the circle to determine the total number of students present today. Ask students what they think will happen if the count starts with a different student and why. Choose a different student to start the count and discuss what happened.

**Teaching Note**

❷ **Games: The Importance of Playing More Than Once** Throughout *Investigations,* games are used as one way to offer students experience and practice with important math ideas. For more information, see **Part 2: How to Use Investigations** in *Implementing Investigations in Kindergarten:* Components of the Program.

MATH WORKSHOP

# ①Using Pictures and Numbers to Represent Quantities

20–35 MIN

Explain that the following four activities are available during this Math Workshop, and that today is the last day that this version of *Grab and Count* will be available. Remind students what each activity entails, what materials are required, and where they are located.

The discussion at the end of this session will focus on common counting errors. Therefore, focus your observations on students' counting, making note of common errors. These may include not saying one number for each cube, repeating or skipping numbers in the sequence, double counting, or skipping some cubes.❶ Because this discussion will be grounded in the context of *Grab and Count,* you may want to ask all students to play at least one round of *Grab and Count* today.❷

## 1A Roll and Record

INDIVIDUALS

For complete details about this activity, see Session 1.4, page 44.

## 1B Counting Jar

INDIVIDUALS

For complete details about this activity, see Session 1.3, page 40.

## 1C Grab and Count

INDIVIDUALS

For complete details about this activity, see Session 1.2, page 34.

## 1D Making a Counting Book

INDIVIDUALS

For complete details about this activity, see Session 1.1, page 28.

10 MIN    CLASS

## ② DISCUSSION
# How Did I Count?

## Math Focus Points for Discussion

◆ Developing strategies for accurately counting and keeping track of quantities up to 12

Gather students for a discussion about counting. Explain that, as you have been watching students count over the course of the last week, you have noticed some things that you would like to discuss.

Grab and display a small handful of cubes. (Do not link the cubes into a train or tower.)

I am going to count this handful of cubes. Watch carefully and listen closely. When I've finished, I'm going to ask what you noticed about my counting.

Count the set of cubes, using one of the errors you have seen students making. For example, leave the cubes in a pile and count them without moving them, being sure to double count and/or skip several cubes.

Okay, I counted the cubes and I think there are [4] cubes. What did you notice about my counting?

Ask students to describe what they noticed and to suggest strategies that may help you count more accurately.❸

[Manuel] said that he thinks I counted some cubes more than once. Would that be correct? Why or why not?

---

### Teaching Note

❸ **Constructive Criticism** In this activity, students critique *your* strategies for counting. At other times, students will be asked to comment on another student's strategy, or to work with a partner to count a set of objects. Therefore, help them think about how to respond in a way that is kind, helpful, and supportive. Remind students that everyone makes mistakes as they learn something new, that mistakes are great opportunities for learning, and that everyone can learn from one another.

**Students might say:**

"You have to count them just once or you won't get the right number."

Why do you think I counted some cubes more than once? Is there something I could do so that would not happen?

**Students might say:**

"You could move the cubes as you count them."

"You could count more slowly so you don't get confused."

Demonstrate the strategies students suggest, which may include putting the cubes in a line or building a tower and then counting the cubes, counting slowly and carefully, and double-checking. Ask students to model these strategies also.

[Rebecca] suggested moving the cubes when I count them. [Rebecca], can you show us how you would do that?

If there is time, grab another handful of cubes and make a different error as you count them; for example, make an error in the counting sequence (omit or repeat a number or mix up the sequence).

SESSION FOLLOW-UP

# 3 Practice

**Student Math Handbook Flip Chart:** Use the *Student Math Handbook Flip Chart* page 19 to reinforce concepts from today's session. See pages 176–181 in the back of this unit.

# Does Order Matter When You Count?

## Math Focus Points

◆ Connecting number words, numerals, and quantities

◆ Representing quantities with pictures, numbers, and/or words

◆ Considering whether order matters when you count

| Today's Plan | | Materials |
|---|---|---|
| **MATH WORKSHOP** <br> ① **Counting and Writing the Numbers** <br> ⓐ *Roll and Record* <br> ⓑ Counting Jar <br> ⓒ Making a Counting Book | 🕐 20–35 MIN | ⓐ • Materials from Session 1.4, p. 43 <br> ⓑ • Materials from Session 1.3, p. 39 <br> ⓒ • Materials from Session 1.1, p. 26 |
| **DISCUSSION** <br> ② **Does Order Matter When You Count?** | 🕐 10 MIN 👥 CLASS | • Counting Jar from Session 1.3, p. 39 <br> • Counting Jar Poster or Counting Jar Booklets |
| **SESSION FOLLOW-UP** <br> ③ **Practice** | | • *Student Math Handbook Flip Chart*, p. 17 |

## Classroom Routines

*Today's Question: Do you have a pet?* On chart paper, create a two-column table entitled "Do you have a pet?" with the label "Yes" at the bottom of one column and "No" at the bottom of the other. Have students write their names above the appropriate label. Count the responses as a class. After counting, have a short discussion about the results of the survey.

**MATH WORKSHOP**

# Counting and Writing the Numbers

20–35 MIN

Explain that the following three activities are available during this Math Workshop. Remind students what each activity entails, what materials are required, and where they are located.

Students who have not yet visited the Counting Jar should begin with this activity because the discussion at the end of this session will focus on it.

## 1A *Roll and Record*

INDIVIDUALS

For complete details on this activity, see Session 1.4, page 44.

**DIFFERENTIATION: Supporting the Range of Learners**

**Extension** Students who are ready for a variation of this activity could record dot images instead of numbers as they play.

| 1 | 2 | 3 | 4 | 5 | 6 |
|---|---|---|---|---|---|

## 1B Counting Jar

INDIVIDUALS

For complete details on this activity, see Session 1.3, page 40.

Remember to look for students who sort the tiles into lines of each color to count them. You will discuss this strategy at the end of this session.

**Making a Counting Book** INDIVIDUALS

For complete details on this activity, see Session 1.1, page 28.

DISCUSSION

# Does Order Matter When You Count?
10 MIN   CLASS

## Math Focus Points for Discussion

◆ Considering whether order matters when you count

Gather your students so that they can see the Counting Jar and the range of ways students recorded the number of tiles in the Counting Jar on your Counting Jar Poster (or in students' Counting Jar Booklets). Ask students who sorted the objects by color in order to count them to model their strategy for the class. (If you did not see any students using this strategy, ask a volunteer to count the objects in the jar by counting the red ones first and then the blue ones.)

This week there were tiles in the Counting Jar. I saw [Abby] do something interesting when she counted the tiles. First, she put the reds together, then she put the blues together, and *then* she counted them. [Abby], would you show us how you counted the tiles?

Encourage students to watch closely while your volunteer counts the tiles.

I noticed that [Abby] counted the reds first and then the blues. I'm wondering if we'll get the same total if someone else counts the blues first, then the reds. What do you think will happen when we switch the order? ❶ ❷

After some discussion, ask another student to count the tiles, starting with the blues and then the reds.

**Math Note**

❶ **Counting in Any Order**  For some, it will not be immediately obvious that this change will not affect the total. This discussion will allow students to begin to think about an important idea in counting; which is that the order in which things are counted or added does not affect the total.

**Professional Development**

❷ **Algebra Connections in This Unit,** p. 16 and **Dialogue Box:** Does the Order Matter?, p. 165

When [Hugo] counted, he got [6] too! What do you think about that? Does order matter when you count a set of objects?

**Students might say:**

"No, because we got the same number when we counted the reds first as we did when we counted the blues first."

"Yes, because it was easier to count the number of reds than the number of blues."

Students will have different responses. It is not important that a conclusion be drawn now; it is important that this idea stay at the forefront as students engage with counting and adding activities throughout the year.

**SESSION FOLLOW-UP**
## ③ Practice

**Student Math Handbook Flip Chart:** Use the *Student Math Handbook Flip Chart* page 17 to reinforce concepts from today's session. See pages 176–181 in the back of this unit.

# Build It

## Math Focus Points

◆ Connecting number words, numerals, and quantities

◆ Creating an equivalent set

◆ Using a Ten-Frame to develop visual images of quantities up to 10

### Vocabulary

**Ten-Frame**

| Today's Plan | | Materials |
|---|---|---|
| **ACTIVITY** ❶ **Introducing** *Build It* <br> 5–10 MIN  CLASS | | • M20–M23* <br> • *Student Activity Book,* p. 7 <br> • Counters |
| **MATH WORKSHOP** ❷ **Using Objects, Numbers, and Pictures to Represent Quantities** <br> 20–30 MIN <br> ②ⓐ *Build It* <br> ②ⓑ *Roll and Record* <br> ②ⓒ Making a Counting Book | | ②ⓐ • Materials from Activity 1 <br> ②ⓑ • Materials from Session 1.4, p. 43 <br> ②ⓒ • Materials from Session 1.1, p. 26 |
| **DISCUSSION** ❸ **Checking In** <br> 5 MIN  CLASS | | |
| **SESSION FOLLOW-UP** ❹ **Practice** | | • *Student Math Handbook Flip Chart,* pp. 11–14 |

*See *Materials to Prepare,* p. 25.

## Classroom Routines

*Calendar: What's Missing?* **Remove two of the days-of-the-week cards on the monthly calendar. Challenge students to tell you which cards are missing and how they know.**

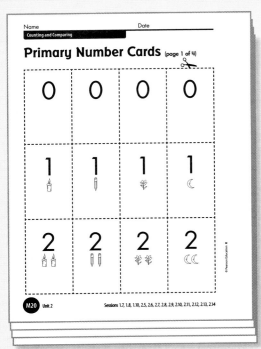

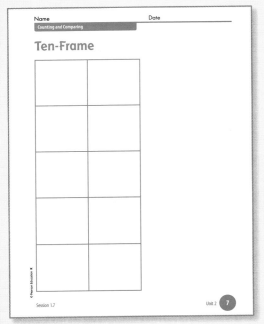

▲ Resource Masters, M20–M23

▲ Student Activity Book, p. 7

### ACTIVITY

5–10 MIN  CLASS

# 1 Introducing *Build It*

Before introducing *Build It,* show students a set of Primary Number Cards (M20–M23). Pass several of the cards around and ask students what they notice.

**Students might say:**

"Each card has a number on it."

"The cards have different pictures on them."

Similarly, show students the Ten-Frame on *Student Activity Book* page 7 and ask them what they notice. Observations should include that there are ten squares altogether, that there are two rows of five squares or five rows of two squares. If no one notices that the objects on some of the cards are arranged like a Ten-Frame, point this out yourself.

Then, explain the game by playing a demonstration game with the class.

Today we are going to play a game called *Build It.* You need a deck of Primary Number Cards, some counters, and a Ten-Frame.

The first thing you do is turn over a Primary Number Card. [Turn over a six.] What card did I turn over? How do you know?

**Students might say:**

"You turned over a six. I know because I counted the candles on the card."

We agree that I turned over a 6. So now I count out six counters and arrange them on my Ten-Frame.

Count out six counters and then place them onto your Ten-Frame, filling one complete row before starting the second row.①

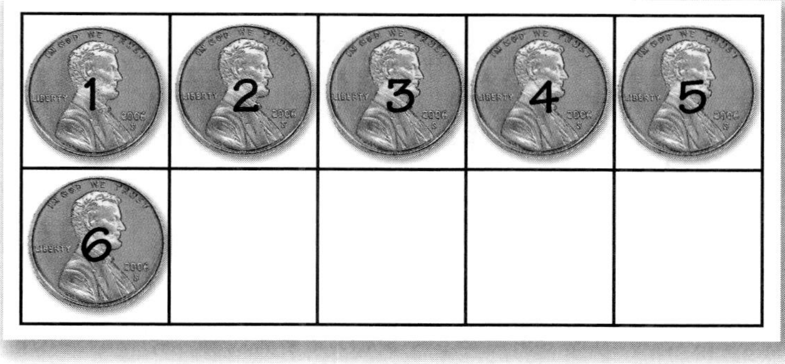


When the class agrees that you have placed as many counters on your Ten-Frame as the number on your Primary Number Card, remove the counters from your Ten-Frame, turn over another Primary Number Card, and demonstrate another round.

MATH WORKSHOP

## 2 Using Objects, Numbers, and Pictures to Represent Quantities

20–30 MIN INDIVIDUALS

Explain that the following three activities are available during this Math Workshop. Remind students of what each activity entails, of what materials are required and where they are located.

Most students should have completed their Counting Books by now. Work with those who have not yet finished them over the course of Sessions 1.7 and 1.8 because you will discuss the Counting Books at the end of Session 1.8.

### 2A Build It

INDIVIDUALS

Students turn over a Primary Number Card to find out how many counters to take. Then they arrange the counters on a Ten-Frame.

#### Teaching Note

① **Placing Counters on the Ten-Frame** Model the game by filling a complete row of 5 before placing any counters in the second row, but know that some students will fill rows of 2 and still others will place them more randomly.

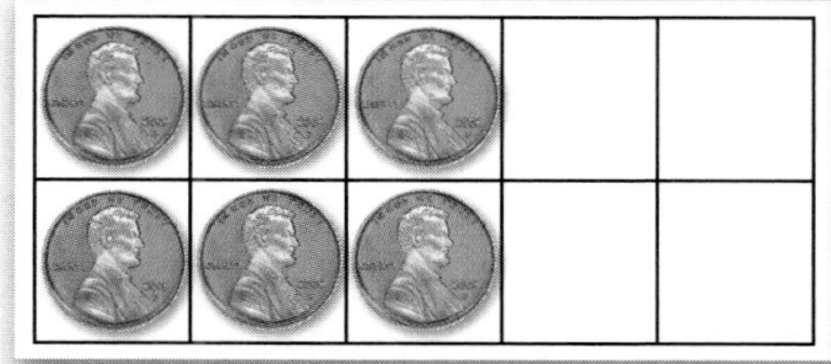

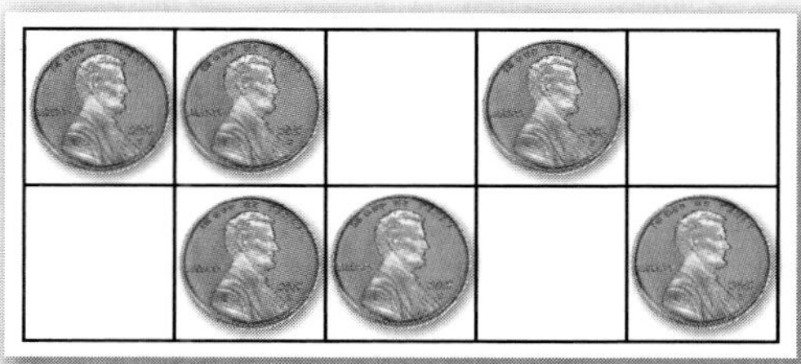

## ONGOING ASSESSMENT: Observing Students at Work

Students practice reading the written numbers, creating a set of a given size, and arranging counters in a Ten-Frame.

- **How do students figure out the number on the card?** Do they recognize the number? Do they count the pictures on the card?

- **Do students make a set that matches the number?** Do they count their counters first and then place them on the Ten-Frame? Do they count them as they place them?

- **How do students arrange the counters on the Ten-Frame?** Do they use the structure of the Ten-Frame to help them count? For example, "Each row has 2, so 2, 4, 6. I have 6 counters" or "This is 3 and this is 3, so there are 6" or "This row has 5 and 1 more is 6."

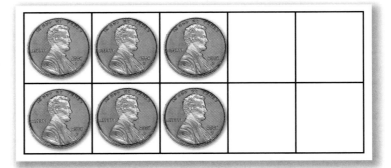

## DIFFERENTIATION: Supporting the Range of Learners

**Intervention** Some students may benefit from playing with only the 1 to 6 cards. If some students are placing the counters randomly on the Ten-Frame, suggest that they place the counters in a way that makes them easier to count, such as finishing a row (of two or five) before starting another.

**ELL** Some English Language Learners might count to themselves in their native language while playing games in this unit. Native language use can be helpful to beginning English Language Learners and therefore should not be prohibited, but you will want to encourage students to count aloud in English as well. Work with students on the pronunciation of particular sounds and numbers as necessary.

## 2B *Roll and Record*

**INDIVIDUALS**

For complete details on this activity, see Session 1.4, page 44.

## 2C Making a Counting Book

**INDIVIDUALS**

For complete details on this activity, see Session 1.1, page 28.

---

### 3 DISCUSSION
# Checking In

**5 MIN   CLASS**

Take this opportunity to discuss any difficulty that you noticed while observing students at work. The topic may be mathematical in nature, such as a strategy you would like all students to consider (e.g., how to figure out the name of the number turned over) or you would like students to discuss, such as showing students several ways to place counters on the Ten-Frame and discussing which arrangements are easiest to count.

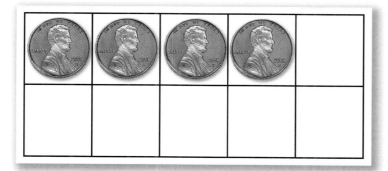

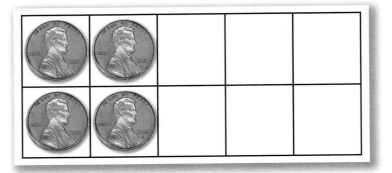

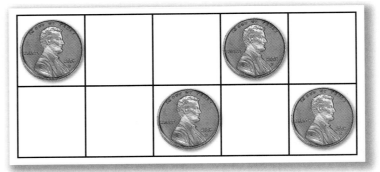

The difficulty could be logistical, for example, clarifying the steps of the activity or management-related (e.g., making choices and working productively during Math Workshop).

Consider checking in with students about which activities they have been choosing (e.g., "Thumbs up if you played *Build It* today. How about *Roll and Record*? Thumbs up if you worked on your Counting Book.") or asking them about the status of their Counting Books, which should be nearly finished.

## SESSION FOLLOW-UP
# 4 Practice

**Student Math Handbook Flip Chart:** Use the *Student Math Handbook Flip Chart* pages 11–14 to reinforce concepts from today's session. See pages 176–181 in the back of this unit.

# Counting Jar

## Math Focus Points

◈ Developing strategies for accurately counting and keeping track of quantities up to 10

◈ Creating an equivalent set

◈ Representing quantities with pictures, numbers, and/or words

### Vocabulary

**size**

| Today's Plan | | Materials |
|---|---|---|
| **①** ACTIVITY<br>**The Counting Jar** | 🕐 5 MIN / 👥 CLASS | • Counting Jar* |
| **②** MATH WORKSHOP<br>**Counting and Creating Equivalent Sets**<br>**2A** Counting Jar<br>**2B** Build It<br>**2C** Roll and Record<br>**2D** Making a Counting Book | 🕐 15–30 MIN | **2A** • Counting Jar from Activity 1; materials for Counting Jar*<br>**2B** • Materials from Session 1.7, p. 55<br>**2C** • Materials from Session 1.4, p. 43<br>**2D** • Materials from Session 1.1, p. 26 |
| **③** DISCUSSION<br>**Counting Books** | 🕐 10 MIN / 👥 CLASS | • Students' completed Counting Books |
| **④** SESSION FOLLOW-UP<br>**Practice** | | • *Student Math Handbook Flip Chart,* p. 20 |

*See *Materials to Prepare,* p. 25.

## Classroom Routines

*Attendance: How Many Have Counted?* Count around the circle to determine the total number of students present. Pause several times during the count to ask students how many people have counted so far. Help students see why the number they say represents the number of students who have counted so far and that the last number represents the total number of students in class today.

## ① ACTIVITY

# The Counting Jar

**5 MIN    CLASS**

Place ten pennies (or other objects) in the Counting Jar and show it to students.

Last week, there were [red and blue tiles] in the Counting Jar. We counted them two different ways to see whether we'd get the same total each time. This week, I put a new set of objects in the Counting Jar.

Briefly review the way this routine works in your class, and explain that this will be one of the activities they can choose during Math Workshop over the next few sessions.

## ② MATH WORKSHOP

# Counting and Creating Equivalent Sets

**15–30 MIN    INDIVIDUALS**

Explain that the following four activities are available during this Math Workshop and that today is the last day of Making a Counting Book. Remind students what each activity entails, what materials are required and where they are located.

## 2A Counting Jar
**INDIVIDUALS**

Students count the objects in the Counting Jar—a set of 10 pennies. They make a set of their own of the same size and then record what they find out.

For complete details on this activity, see Session 1.3, page 40.

## 2B *Build It*

**INDIVIDUALS**

For complete details on this activity, see Session 1.7, page 56.

## 2C *Roll and Record*

**INDIVIDUALS**

For complete details on this activity, see Session 1.4, page 44.

##  Making a Counting Book

INDIVIDUALS

For complete details on this activity, see Session 1.1, page 28.

### DISCUSSION
# 3 Counting Books

10 MIN  CLASS

## Math Focus Points for Discussion

◆ Creating an equivalent set

Bring students together to share their Counting Books. Begin by asking students to open their completed Counting Books to their 5 page.

Look at your 5 page. What are some of the ways that you showed 5?

Ask several volunteers to share what they did. Encourage students to compare different drawings and challenge them to consider whether both show 5.

[Caitlin] drew five [flowers]. Look how big they are! They take up her whole page. . . . [Victor] used stamps to make five [trees]. They are different sizes. Do you see them?

On chart paper or the board, draw two sets of 5 that are similar to the students' work. For example, draw five large houses that take up a great deal of space, and, beneath them, five small stars.

**Professional Development**

❶ **Teacher Note:** Counting Is More Than 1, 2, 3, p. 151

I have a question. Did [Caitlin] and [Victor] both show 5? How can those both be five? They look so different.

**Students might say:**

"They both have 5 because . . . count them: 1, 2, 3, 4, 5. 5 houses and 1, 2, 3, 4, 5. 5 stars."

"I think there are more houses because look, they take up all this space."

Expect a range of responses. Students who think there are more houses than stars because the houses take up so much more room than the stars cannot yet conserve quantities. They will come to understand this important idea through varied counting experiences and discussions such as this one. ❶

---

**SESSION FOLLOW-UP**

## 4 Practice

**Student Math Handbook Flip Chart:** Use the *Student Math Handbook Flip Chart* page 20 to reinforce concepts from today's session. See pages 176–181 in the back of this unit.

# Inventories

## Math Focus Points

- Developing strategies for accurately counting and keeping track of quantities up to 12
- Representing quantities with pictures, numbers, and/or words

### Vocabulary

**inventory**
**double-check**

| Today's Plan | | | Materials |
|---|---|---|---|
| **ACTIVITY** **① Introducing Inventories** | 5–10 MIN | CLASS | • *Student Activity Book*, p. 8 <br> • A prepared Inventory Bag* |
| **ACTIVITY** **② Inventory Bags** | 15–25 MIN | PAIRS | • *Student Activity Book*, p. 8 <br> • M3 ☑ * <br> • M24* <br> • Prepared Inventory Bags; art supplies |
| **DISCUSSION** **③ How Did You Record?** | 5–10 MIN | CLASS | |
| **SESSION FOLLOW-UP** **④ Practice** | | | • *Student Math Handbook Flip Chart*, pp. 17, 18, 19 |

*See *Materials to Prepare*, p. 25.

## Classroom Routines

*Today's Question: Would you rather play inside or outside?* On chart paper, create a two-column table entitled "Would you rather play inside or outside?" with the label "Inside" at the bottom of one column and "Outside" at the bottom of the other. Have students write their names above the appropriate label. Count the responses as a class. After counting, have a short discussion about the results of the survey.

**ACTIVITY**

5–10 MIN CLASS

# Introducing Inventories

Show students one of the inventory bags you have prepared.

We have many different materials in our classroom and some of them are things that we use up, like pencils. I count those things so that I know when we are running out and I need to order more. Many people do this kind of counting. It even has a special name.

When we count to find out how many of something we have in a classroom or a store or in our house, it's called "taking an inventory." This means that we count to find out how many of something there is. Today we're going to take an inventory of some of the materials in our classroom. I made bags that hold the things you'll be counting.

Show students the contents of the sample inventory bag.

For this activity you and a partner will get a bag. Your job is to work together to figure out how many objects are inside. Then, each of you makes a representation, or picture, that shows what's in the bag and how many there are in the bag.

Ask a student to be your partner so that you can demonstrate. Ask the student to count the items in the bag. Then, count them yourself and come up with a different answer than your student volunteer did. That way, you can talk about what to do when this happens and discuss ways to disagree respectfully.

When [Raul] counted the buttons in our bag, he got [6]. When I counted the buttons in our bag, I got [5]. Can we both be right? How can we double-check?

**Students might say:**

"We could count again while everyone watches."

Discuss other strategies for resolving such discrepancies, such as counting the objects in a different way to double-check. Encourage students to work together to count the objects, but acknowledge that sometimes it will be hard for partners to come to an agreement. When this happens, each student's representation should show how many objects he or she thinks are in the bag. There will be time to discuss discrepancies after the inventories are completed.

After you and your volunteer student partner have agreed on the number of objects in the bag, briefly discuss *Student Activity Book* page 8. Model how to fill in the letter of the bag inventoried, and point out that the name of the item in the bag is written on the bag in case students want to use words when they record.

What could I write or draw on this sheet to show someone what we found out about Bag [A]? What's the important information about Bag [A]?

After students have shared their ideas, summarize what students will note on *Student Activity Book* page 8: the letter on the bag, the kind of object in the bag, and the number of objects in the bag. Allow students to generate their own ways of recording, rather than demonstrating possible methods.

Name _____ Date _____
Counting and Comparing

**My Inventory Bag**
Show what was in your bag.
Show how many.

Bag

8    Unit 2                                    Session 1.9

▲ **Student Activity Book, p. 8;**
**Resource Masters, M24**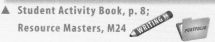

## Math Notes

**1 Extending the Work with Inventory Bags** One way to extend the work with Inventory Bags is to ask all students in your class to inventory one or two bags that you specify over the course of the next few sessions. Then, you can post all of the representations for a particular bag in one place and discuss the variety of ways students chose to represent the contents of the same bag. If students have found different totals for the same bag, that, too, could spark an interesting discussion.

**2 Continuing to Assess Students' Counting** Given that students are expected to be able to count a set of ten objects accurately (Benchmark 1) by the end of this unit, and that they have spent eight sessions working on counting activities, this is a good time to look closely at students' strategies for counting. Use Assessment Checklist: Counting (M3) to keep track of your observations.

## Professional Development

**3 Teacher Note:** Assessing Students' Counting, p. 153

## Teaching Note

**4 Assembling a Portfolio** Students' representations on *Student Activity Book* page 8 or My Inventory Bag (M24) provide examples of how they are representing quantities. Students will revisit Inventory Bags later in the year, so including another student representation of Inventory Bags from a later unit provides an opportunity to assess students' growth.

### ACTIVITY

## 2 Inventory Bags

15–25 MIN   PAIRS

Pairs take a bag and count the items in it. Then students record what they found out on *Student Activity Book* page 8. ① ② ③ ④

### ONGOING ASSESSMENT: Observing Students at Work

Students count a set of objects and find a way to represent that quantity on paper.

- **How do students count the objects in the bag?** Do they organize the objects in any way? Do they count each item once and only once? Do they double-check?

- **Do students have a way of keeping track of which objects have already been counted, such as touching or moving each object as they count it?**

- **What happens if a pair gets two different totals? Do students notice?** Do they double-check? Count the objects again? Count them in a different way?

- **How do students record their work?** Can you tell which bag they had? What was in the bag? How many were in the bag?

As you circulate, take note of bags for which there are disagreements to discuss in Session 1.10.

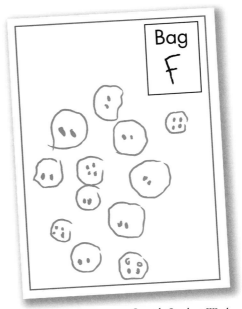

*Sample Student Work*

*Sample Student Work*

*Sample Student Work*

---

## DIFFERENTIATION: Supporting the Range of Learners

**Extension** Pairs who finish early can trade bags, do another inventory, and then compare their results with each other. If no one is available to trade bags, pairs who finish early can inventory one of the extra bags you prepared.

**ELL** Consider the type of pairing that will be most effective for English Language Learners during partnered activities. A beginning English Language Learner, for example, might benefit from working with a partner who shares his or her native language but is more proficient in English, while a more advanced English Language Learner might work successfully with a native English-speaking peer.

### DISCUSSION

# 3 How Did You Record?

**5–10 MIN  CLASS**

## Math Focus Points for Discussion

◆ Representing quantities with pictures, numbers, and/or words

Bring students together to share their work. Focus the discussion on the different methods they had for representing their inventories. Ask volunteers to show and explain their work to the class.

[Beth] drew a picture of each object in the bag. Did anyone else draw a picture of each item in the bag? Raise your hand if you did. Did anyone show the information in a different way? I see that [Jae] used numbers. That's a different way. Did anyone else use numbers? Raise your hands.

By asking for a show of hands for each method discussed, you can acknowledge everyone's work without taking the time for each child to share individually.

### SESSION FOLLOW-UP

# 4 Practice

**Student Math Handbook Flip Chart:** Use the *Student Math Handbook Flip Chart* pages 17, 18, 19 to reinforce concepts from today's session. See pages 176–181 in the back of this unit.

# Strategies for Accurate Counting

## Math Focus Points

◆ Developing strategies for accurately counting and keeping track of quantities up to 12

◆ Representing quantities with pictures, numbers, and/or words

| Today's Plan | | Materials |
|---|---|---|
| **MATH WORKSHOP**<br>**① Counting Objects, Representing Quantities**<br>**1A** Inventory Bags<br>**1B** Counting Jar<br>**1C** *Build It*<br>**1D** *Roll and Record* | 20–35 MIN | **1A** • Materials from Session 1.9, p. 65<br>**1B** • Materials from Session 1.8, p. 61<br>**1C** • Materials from Session 1.7, p. 55<br>**1D** • Materials from Session 1.4, p. 43 |
| **DISCUSSION**<br>**② Strategies for Accurate Counting** | 10 MIN CLASS | • One or two Inventory Bags |
| **SESSION FOLLOW-UP**<br>**③ Practice** | | • *Student Activity Book,* p. 9 |

## Classroom Routines

*Calendar: How Many Days . . . ?* Students use the calendar to determine how many days since a class event or holiday that happened during the month. Discuss students' strategies for determining the number of days.

MATH WORKSHOP

**20–35 MIN**

# Counting Objects, Representing Quantities

Explain that the following four activities are available during Math Workshop and that today is the last day that both *Roll and Record* and *Build It* will be available. Remind students what each activity entails, what materials are required, and where they are located.

## 1A Inventory Bags

For complete details on this activity, see Session 1.9, page 66.

## 1B Counting Jar

For complete details on this activity, see Session 1.3, page 40 and Session 1.8, page 62.

## 1C *Build It*

For complete details on this activity, see Session 1.7, page 56.

## 1D *Roll and Record*

For complete details on this activity, see Session 1.4, page 44.

DISCUSSION

**10 MIN    CLASS**

# Strategies for Accurate Counting

## Math Focus Points For Discussion

◆ Developing strategies for accurately counting and keeping track of quantities up to 12

Gather students for another brief discussion about Inventory Bags.

What happened if you counted and got one number and then your partner counted and got a different number? Does that matter?

Use this discussion to focus on strategies for counting and keeping track of or organizing a count. Students will have a variety of ideas about why different people came up with different numbers. Encourage them to think about possible reasons and to avoid "Because I know I'm right" answers.❶

---

**SESSION FOLLOW-UP**

## Practice

 **Practice:** For reinforcement of this unit's content, have students complete *Student Activity Book* page 9.

**Professional Development**

❶ **Dialogue Box:** Is It 10 or 11?, p. 167

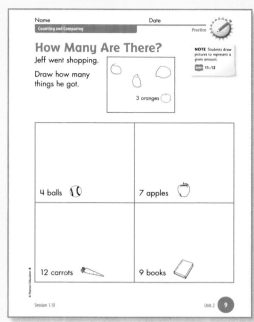

▲ **Student Activity Book, p. 9**

## Mathematical Emphases

**Linear Measurement** Understanding length

**Math Focus Points**

◆ Directly comparing two objects to determine which is longer

◆ Sorting objects into two categories according to length

◆ Developing language to describe and compare lengths (long, longer than, short, shorter than, the same, equal to)

**Counting and Quantity** Developing strategies for accurately counting a set of objects by ones

**Math Focus Points**

◆ Developing strategies for accurately counting and keeping track of quantities up to 12

◆ Counting backwards

◆ Connecting number words, numerals, and quantities

**Counting and Quantity** Developing the idea of equivalence

**Math Focus Points**

◆ Creating an equivalent set

**Counting and Quantity** Developing an understanding of the magnitude and position of numbers

**Math Focus Points**

◆ Comparing two (or more) quantities to determine which is more

◆ Developing language for comparing quantities (more, greater, less, fewer, most, least, fewest, same, and equal to)

◆ Ordering quantities from least to most

# Comparing

| | Student Activity Book | Student Math Handbook Flip Chart | Professional Development: Read Ahead of Time | |
|---|---|---|---|---|
| **SESSION 2.1**    p. 82 | | | | |
| **Measurement Towers** Students compare classroom objects to a tower of 10 cubes to determine which is longer. Math Workshop focuses on counting and comparing. | 10 | 37 | • **Teacher Note:** Learning About Length: Direct Comparison, p. 160 | |
| **SESSION 2.2**    p. 88 | | | | |
| **How Did You Measure?** Students continue counting and comparing, and discuss strategies for comparing objects to see which is longer. | | 37 | • **Dialogue Box:** How Did You Compare?, p. 168 | |
| **SESSION 2.3**    p. 91 | | | | |
| **Counting Backwards** Students continue to count and compare. Discussion focuses on counting backwards. | | 11, 37 | | |
| **SESSION 2.4**    p. 94 | | | | |
| **Grab and Count: Compare** Students count and build a tower for each of two handfuls of cubes and compare them to see which is longer. Discussion focuses on how to sort objects when it is hard to tell which is longer. | | 21, 22, 23 | • **Teacher Note:** *Grab and Count* and Its Variations, p. 161 <br> • **Dialogue Box:** You Have to Look at the Long Side, p. 170 | |
| **SESSION 2.5**    p. 100 | | | | |
| **The Game of Compare** Students learn, play, and discuss *Compare*, a card game in which players each turn over a Primary Number Card and compare the two numbers to determine which is larger. | | 21, 22, 23 | • **Dialogue Box:** Playing *Compare* with a Partner, p. 172 | |

*Attendance*
- **No materials needed**

*Calendar*
- **Monthly calendar. Use pocket calendar.**

*Today's Question*
- **Today's Question charts for Sessions 2.2, 2.5, 2.8, 2.11, and 2.14.**
  **See instructions on pages 88, 100, 117, 133, and 145.**

| Materials to Gather | Materials to Prepare |
|---|---|
| • **Materials for Inventory Bags** See Session 1.9, p. 65.<br>• **Materials for the Counting Jar** See Session 1.8, p. 61. | • **M25, Longer or Shorter** Make copies. (1 per student)<br>• **M26, Assessment Checklist: Comparing Lengths** ☑ Make copies. (3–4 per class as needed)<br>• **Measuring Tables** Set up one larger or several smaller Measuring Tables.<br>• **Measurement Collection** On each Measuring Table, place objects of different lengths, including several that are shorter than, longer than, and about the same length as a tower of 10 cubes. Include items with more than one possible dimension to measure, including some that are easy to stand vertically.<br>• **Connecting cubes** On each Measuring Table, place a bin of cubes of one color and create a tower of 10 cubes in another color. |
| • **Materials for Measuring Table** See Session 2.1.<br>• **Materials for Inventory Bags** See Session 1.9, p. 65.<br>• **Materials for Counting Jar** See Session 1.8, p. 61.<br>• **Tower of 10 cubes** (of one color)<br>• **Measurement Collection** See Session 2.1. | |
| • **Materials for Measuring Table** See Session 2.1.<br>• **Materials for Inventory Bags** See Session 1.9, p. 25.<br>• **Materials for Counting Jar** (and Counting Jar Poster or Booklets) See Sessions 1.6, p. 51 and 1.8, p. 61. | • **Counting Jar** Place 10 pennies in the Counting Jar (if you don't have it set up this way already.) |
| • **Materials for Measuring Table** See Session 2.1.<br>• **Materials for Inventory Bags** See Session 1.9, p. 65.<br>• **Connecting cubes** (sorted by color)<br>• **Coloring Materials** Crayons or markers (same color as connecting cubes) | • **M27, Cube Strips** Make copies. (5–6 per student, plus extras as needed) Cut along dotted lines.<br>• **M28, Assessment Checklist: Comparing Quantities** ☑ Make copies. (3–4 per class as needed) |
| • **Primary Number Cards** (1 deck per pair, with Wild Cards removed; from Investigation 1)<br>• **Connecting cubes** (10 per student and then 20 per pair) | • **M29–M30, Family Letter** Make copies. (1 per student) |

☑ Checklist Available

# Comparing, *continued*

| | Student Activity Book | Student Math Handbook Flip Chart | Professional Development: Read Ahead of Time | |
|---|---|---|---|---|
| **SESSION 2.6** p. 105 | | | | |
| **Comparing Two Inventory Bags** Students continue counting and comparing quantities. Then the class compares the contents of the two Inventory Bags. | | 21, 22, 23 | • **Teacher Note:** Counting Is More Than 1, 2, 3, p. 151 | |
| **SESSION 2.7** p. 110 | | | | |
| **Letters in Our Names** Students hear a story about someone with a very long name and determine how many letters are in that name. Then, they count how many letters are in their names and build cube towers to represent them. | 11 | | | |
| **SESSION 2.8** p. 117 | | | | |
| **Counting Jar** A name tower for the very long name discussed in Session 2.7 is placed in the Counting Jar. Students continue to count and compare quantities. | | 20, 21, 22, 23 | | |
| **SESSION 2.9** p. 121 | | | | |
| **Comparing Names** Students use their name towers to compare the lengths of the names in their class. Discussion focuses on a longer/shorter sort that includes problematic objects. | 12 | 21, 22, 23, 37 | | |
| **SESSION 2.10** p. 128 | | | | |
| **Grab and Count: Ordering** Students are introduced to a new variation of *Grab and Count* that involves putting 4 handfuls of cubes in order. Discussion focuses on why the student with the shortest (or longest) name has no names in the Shorter (or Longer) Than My Name category. | 12, 13 | 24 | • **Dialogue Box:** Comparing and Ordering Towers, p. 174 | |

| Materials to Gather | Materials to Prepare |
|---|---|
| • **Tower of 10 cubes** (of one color)<br>• **Students' towers of 10 cubes** (from Session 2.1)<br>• **Materials for** *Compare*   See Session 2.5.<br>• **Materials for** *Grab and Count: Compare*<br>  See Session 2.4.<br>• **Two Inventory Bags**   See Session 1.9, p. 65. | |
| • **A book about a character with a very long name**<br>  Suggestions include *Chrysanthemum* by Kevin Henkes,<br>  *Rumplestiltskin* by Paul O. Zelinsky or *Jacob Grimm* or *Tikki Tikki*<br>  *Tembo* by Arlene Mosel.<br>• **Connecting cubes** (sort by color)<br>• **Materials for Longer/Shorter Hunt**   See Session 2.6.<br>• **Materials for** *Compare*   See Session 2.5.<br>• **Materials for** *Grab and Count: Compare*   See Session 2.4. | • **Name Cards**   Write each student's first name on an index card.<br>• **Dot Stickers**   Write letters of the alphabet on them. You will need enough of each letter<br>  to spell each child's name. |
| • **Counting Jar** (with a very long name tower)<br>• **Materials for Counting Jar** (as you have it set up)<br>• **Materials for Name Towers**   See Session 2.7.<br>• **Materials for Longer/Shorter Hunt**   See Session 2.6.<br>• **Materials for** *Compare*   See Session 2.5.<br>• **Materials for** *Grab and Count: Compare*   See Session 2.4. | • **Name Tower**   Prepare a name tower for the very long name discussed in Session 2.7.<br>• **Index Card**   Write the very long name on the index card. |
| • **Students' Name Towers** (from Sessions 2.7 and 2.8)<br>• **Materials for Counting Jar**   See Session 2.8.<br>• **Materials for Longer/Shorter Hunt**   See Session 2.6.<br>• **Materials for** *Compare*   See Session 2.5.<br>• **Tower of 10 cubes** | • **Two Index Cards**   Label one card "Longer Than My Tower" and another card "Shorter Than<br>  My Tower"<br>• **Subset of Longer/Shorter Hunt Objects**   Choose several objects that students have placed<br>  in the "Longer Than My Tower" category and several from the "Shorter Than My Tower"<br>  category. Also include several erroneous objects in each category. |
| • **Connecting Cubes** (sort by color)<br>• **Coloring Materials** (same color as cubes)<br>• **Materials for Comparing Names**   See Session 2.9.<br>• **Materials for Counting Jar**   See Session 2.8.<br>• **Materials for** *Compare*   See Session 2.5. | • **M27, Cube Strips**   Make copies. Cut along dotted lines. (5–6 per student, plus extras) |

# Comparing, *continued*

| | Student Activity Book | Student Math Handbook Flip Chart | Professional Development: Read Ahead of Time | |
|---|---|---|---|---|
| **SESSION 2.11** p. 133 | | | | |
| **Ordering Names** Students continue to count, compare, and order as they use the name towers to order the names of four classmates from the least number of letters to the most. | 15 | 24 | | |
| **SESSION 2.12** p. 138 | | | | |
| **Ordering Cards** Students choose four Primary Number Cards and put them in order from smallest to largest. Students continue to practice counting, comparing, and ordering. | 16 | 24 | | |
| **SESSION 2.13** p. 142 | | | | |
| **End-of-Unit Assessment and Ordering** While students continue to count, compare, and order quantities during Math Workshop, those who have not yet met the benchmarks for this unit meet individually with the teacher. Depending on which benchmarks they have or have not met, they count a set of ten objects, compare a tower of ten cubes to several objects to say which is longer, and/or play a few rounds of *Compare* with the teacher. | 17 | | | |
| **SESSION 2.14** p. 145 | | | | |
| **End-of-Unit Assessment and Ordering Our Names** Students continue to count, compare, and order quantities during Math Workshop, while students who have not yet met the benchmarks meet individually with the teacher. Discussion focuses on putting students' name towers in order. | | 21, 22, 23, 24 | | |

| Materials to Gather | Materials to Prepare |
|---|---|
| • **Students' Name Towers** (from Sessions 2.7 and 2.8)<br>• **Materials from** *Grab and Count: Ordering*<br>  See Session 2.10.<br>• **Materials for** *Compare*  See Session 2.5. | |
| • **Primary Number Cards** (1 deck, with Wild Cards removed; from Investigation 1)<br>• **Materials from Ordering Names**  See Session 2.11.<br>• **Materials from** *Grab and Count: Ordering*  See Session 2.10.<br>• **Materials for** *Compare*  See Session 2.5. | |
| • **Connecting cubes** (one bin)<br>• **Primary Number Cards** (1 deck, with Wild Cards removed; from Investigation 1)<br>• **Materials for** *Ordering Cards*  See Session 2.12.<br>• **Materials from Ordering Names**  See Session 2.11.<br>• **Materials from** *Grab and Count: Ordering*  See Session 2.10.<br>• **Materials for** *Compare*  See Session 2.5.<br>• **Completed and blank copies of Assessment Checklists M3, M26, M28** ☑ | • **Objects to Compare**  Select 3 objects to compare. One object is shorter than a tower of 10 cubes, one is longer, and one is about the same length.<br>• **M3, M26, M28, Assessment Checklists** ☑  Make copies. (as needed; from Sessions 1.1, 2.1, 2.4) |
| • **Students' Name Towers** (from Sessions 2.7 and 2.8)<br>• **Materials for** *Ordering Cards*  See Session 2.12.<br>• **Materials from Ordering Names**  See Session 2.11.<br>• **Materials from** *Grab and Count: Ordering*  See Session 2.10.<br>• **Materials for** *Compare*  See Session 2.5.<br>• **Materials for End-of-Unit Assessments** (from Session 2.13, p. 142) | |

☑  Checklist Available

**Investigation 2 Planner** 81

# Measurement Towers

## Math Focus Points

- Directly comparing two objects to determine which is longer
- Sorting objects into two categories according to length
- Developing language to describe and compare lengths (long, longer than, short, shorter than, the same, equal to)

### Vocabulary

| | |
|---|---|
| compare | longer |
| taller | shorter |
| measure | |

## Today's Plan

| | Materials |
|---|---|
| **ACTIVITY**<br>**1 Using Towers to Compare**    5–10 MIN   CLASS | • A tower of 10 connecting cubes of one color*; objects from a Measurement Collection* |
| **ACTIVITY**<br>**2 Introducing the Measuring Table**    5–10 MIN   CLASS   GROUPS | • *Student Activity Book,* p. 10<br>• M25*<br>• Connecting cubes of one color; a tower of 10 connecting cubes of another color; objects from a Measurement Collection |
| **MATH WORKSHOP**<br>**3 Counting and Comparing Lengths**    15–20 MIN<br>  **3A** Measuring Table<br>  **3B** Inventory Bags<br>  **3C** Counting Jar | **3A** • *Student Activity Book,* p. 10<br>  • M26 ☑ *<br>  • Connecting cubes (sorted by color); 10-cube tower; Measurement Collection<br>**3B** • Materials from Session 1.9, p. 65<br>**3C** • Materials from Session 1.8, p. 61 |
| **DISCUSSION**<br>**4 Checking In**    5 MIN   CLASS | |
| **SESSION FOLLOW-UP**<br>**5 Practice** | • *Student Math Handbook Flip Chart,* p. 37 |

*See *Materials to Prepare,* p. 77.

## Classroom Routines

*Attendance: What if We Start With . . . ?* **Count around the circle to determine the total number of students present today. Ask students what they think will happen if the count starts with a different student and why. Choose a different student to start the count and discuss what happened.**

ACTIVITY

# 1 Using Towers to Compare

5–10 MIN  CLASS

**Professional Development**

❶ **Teacher Note:** Learning About Length: Direct Comparison, p. 160

To introduce this activity, you will need a tower of ten cubes of the same color and several objects from a Measurement Collection. Include at least one object that is shorter than your cube tower, one that is longer, and one that is about the same length. Also include an object that has more than one possible dimension to measure (e.g., a book or a box) and another that is easy to compare by standing it vertically (e.g., a bottle or a paper towel roll).

Gather students so that they can see the objects and your cube tower.

Sometimes, to see how big something is, we compare it with something else. For example, we may stand two people side by side and compare them to see who is taller. We line them up next to each other, to see who is taller. Today we're going to use this tower of ten cubes that way. We will compare the tower to other things to measure them. Who sees something in this collection that looks longer than the cube tower?

Ask a volunteer to choose an object from your collection. Encourage students to find the longest dimension of an object when comparing it to the cube tower.

Okay, [Abby], you think this box is longer than my cube tower. Why do you think so? How can we find out for sure? Can you show us how you would do it? . . . Does someone have a different way to compare them? Can you show us? . . . Does it matter how you hold the box? The tower? Why do you think so?

Ask students to notice how different volunteers compare the tower to the object. Some students will not attend to the longest dimension of an object, and others will hold the tower in a way that does not result in an accurate comparison. You may also find that students verbalize one idea and do something quite different.

Use this opportunity to discuss different methods of comparing the length of two objects so that students are exposed to several strategies. However, do not expect all students to understand or even use these strategies. You will have a chance to discuss these issues in more detail in Session 2.2, after students have had experience comparing the length of their own tower of ten to many objects.❶

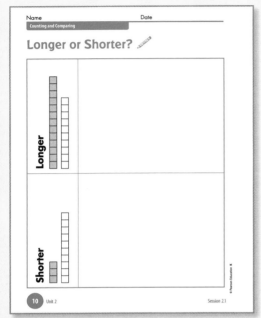

▲ **Student Activity Book, p.10; Resource Masters, M25**

Who sees something in this collection that is shorter than my cube tower? . . . [Jack] says the eraser is shorter. What do we mean when we say that the eraser is shorter than my tower?

How could you compare them to show which is shorter?

### Students might say:

"You could line them up side by side to see which one is lower."

Does someone have a different way?

Discuss other strategies for comparing objects to the tower.

**ACTIVITY**

5–10 MIN   CLASS   GROUPS

## ❷ Introducing the Measuring Table❷

Show students a Measurement Collection. Explain that the Measuring Table is one of the activities students can choose during Math Workshop today and for the next few days.

If you choose the Measuring Table, you are going to measure objects by comparing them to a tower of ten cubes. So your first job is to make a tower with exactly ten cubes in it.

Explain that there will be a model tower at each station and that students should count very carefully and check with other students to make sure that everyone has ten cubes in their tower.

After you make sure that your tower has ten cubes, measure each object in the collection and decide whether it is *longer* or *shorter* than your tower of 10. You're going to put all of the objects in your collection into two groups: "things longer than my tower" and "things shorter than my tower."

**Teaching Note**

❸ **Objects That Are Hard to Place**  Some students feel the need for a third category: Things about the same size as my tower or things that are so close to my cube tower that I can't tell which is longer.

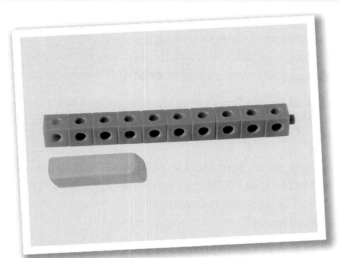

*Students line up the end of the object with the end of the cube tower.*

Show students *Student Activity Book* page 10. Point out the words *longer* and *shorter,* and explain that students can record their results in any way that makes sense to them as long as they can share which objects they think are longer and shorter than their tower. You may demonstrate one way to record the objects you have discussed as a class by drawing a quick sketch of each in the appropriate column.

**MATH WORKSHOP**

15–20 MIN

# ③ Counting and Comparing Lengths

Explain that the following three activities are available during Math Workshop. Remind students what each activity entails, what materials are required, and where they are located.

## 3A Measuring Table

INDIVIDUALS

Students make a tower of ten cubes to use as a measurement standard, and compare their tower to each item in a Measurement Collection. They sort the objects into two groups: things that are longer than the tower and things that are shorter than the tower.❸

**ONGOING ASSESSMENT: Observing Students at Work**

Students compare the length of objects to a tower of ten cubes to see which are longer and shorter.

## Teaching Note

**❹ Assessing Students as They Measure** By the end of this unit, students are expected to be able to directly compare two objects and say which is longer (Benchmark 2). This means that they compare the longest dimensions, hold the objects straight, and line the ends of each object up to compare them. Use Assessment Checklist: Comparing Length (M26) to keep track of your observations about students' strategies for comparing the length of two objects over the course of this Investigation. For more information, see **Teacher Note:** Learning About Length: Direct Comparison, p. 160.

- **How confident and accurate are students in counting out ten cubes?** What kinds of errors do you notice? How do students make sure that they have ten? Do they recount? Do students compare their tower with a neighbor's or with the model tower?

- **How do students compare objects to a tower of ten cubes?** Do they stand them next to each other? Lay them side by side? Do they align them at one end?

- **How do students sort the objects?** Do they compare them directly to their towers? Do they sort some without comparing? How do they sort objects that have one dimension close to the same length as their tower?

- **How do students explain their reasoning for a given object?** Do they use vocabulary such as *longer than* and *shorter than*?

As you observe, keep track of some of the different methods students use to compare objects to their towers to discuss at the end of this Session.❹

### Assessment Checklist: Comparing Lengths

| Student | Lines up the end of the objects to compare them | Holds the objects parallel to each other | Compares the longest dimension(s) | Notes |
|---|---|---|---|---|
| Yoshio | | | ✓ | Holds the pencil near the tower and quickly decides it is smaller. |
| Rebecca | ✓ | ✓ | ✓ | Carefully places end of book on table + bottom of tower on table examines + compares objects closely |
| Raul | ✓ | ✓ | ✓ | |
| Mary | ✓ | ✓ | | Compares tower to longer dimension, for some objects; shorter for others |
| Abby | | ✓ | ✓ | |
| Laquinta | ✓ | ✓ | ✓ | Says eraser is longer than tower, but it isn't. Does she understand the word "longer"? |
| | | | | |

## DIFFERENTIATION: Supporting the Range of Learners

**Intervention** If you come across students who do not have ten cubes in their towers, show them how to compare their tower to the model and how to add or remove cubes as necessary.

**ELL** Students need to understand the concepts of same and different, as well as the use of comparatives, in order to make comparisons throughout this Investigation. To make these concepts concrete for English Language Learners, create two 5-cube towers and one 10-cube tower in the same color. Examine the towers with the students, emphasizing the words *compare, same, different, longer,* and *shorter.* Then have each student create a tower and compare it to another student's tower, using similar vocabulary.

## 3B Inventory Bags

**INDIVIDUALS**

For complete details about this activity, see Session 1.9, page 66.

## 3C Counting Jar

**INDIVIDUALS**

For complete details about this activity, see Session 1.3, page 40.

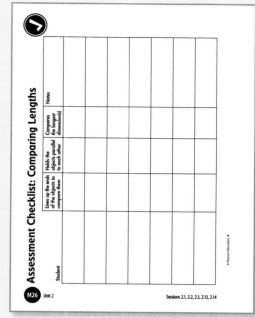

▲ **Resource Masters, M26** ✓

**DISCUSSION**

**5 MIN     CLASS**

# ④ Checking In

Take this opportunity to discuss any difficulties that you noticed while observing students at work. The topic may be mathematical in nature, such as a strategy you would like all students to consider—lining up the edge of two objects to compare them, or a common error you would like students to discuss, for example measuring a dimension of an object that is not the longest dimension.

The difficulty may be logistical, such as clarifying the steps of the activity or management-related, for example noise level, keeping Measurement Collections intact, working independently and productively.

If you introduced the Measuring Table to small groups during Math Workshop, you may want to check in to see which students have not yet done this activity by saying,

*Raise your hand if you didn't work at the Measuring Table today.*

Have those students begin at the Measuring Table tomorrow.

**SESSION FOLLOW-UP**

# ⑤ Practice

**Student Math Handbook Flip Chart:** Use the *Student Math Handbook Flip Chart* page 37 to reinforce concepts from today's session. See pages 176–181 in the back of this unit.

# How Did You Measure?

## Math Focus Points

- Directly comparing two objects to determine which is longer
- Sorting objects into two categories according to length
- Developing language to describe and compare lengths (long, longer than, short, shorter than, the same, equal to)

| Today's Plan | Materials |
|---|---|
| **MATH WORKSHOP** <br> **① Counting and Comparing Lengths** <br> **1A** Measuring Table <br> **1B** Inventory Bags <br> **1C** Counting Jar <br> *20–35 MIN* | **1A** • Materials from Session 2.1, p. 82 <br> **1B** • Materials from Session 1.9, p. 65 <br> **1C** • Materials from Session 1.8, p. 61 |
| **DISCUSSION** <br> **② How Did You Measure?** <br> *10 MIN   CLASS* | • Tower of 10 cubes; Measurement Collection |
| **SESSION FOLLOW-UP** <br> **③ Practice** | • *Student Math Handbook Flip Chart,* p. 37 |

## Classroom Routines

*Today's Question: Would you rather eat apples or grapes?*  On chart paper, create a two-column table entitled "Would you rather eat apples or grapes?" with the label "Apples" at the bottom of one column and "Grapes" at the bottom of the other. Have students write their names above the appropriate label. Count the responses as a class. After counting, have a short discussion about the results of the survey.

**MATH WORKSHOP**

# Counting and Comparing Lengths

20–35 MIN

Explain that the following three activities are available during Math Workshop. Remind students of what each activity entails, what materials are required, and where they are located.

Students who have not yet visited the Measuring Table should do so today in preparation for the discussion at the end of this Session.

## 1A Measuring Table

INDIVIDUALS

For complete details about this activity, see Session 2.1, page 84.

Keep track of the methods students use to compare lengths, and record any discrepancies that arise (such as an object that some students place in the shorter group and others in the longer group) for the discussions in this Session and in Session 2.4.

## 1B Inventory Bags

INDIVIDUALS

For complete details about this activity, see Session 1.9, page 66.

## 1C Counting Jar

INDIVIDUALS

For complete details about this activity, see Session 1.3, page 40.

**DISCUSSION**

# How Did You Measure?

10 MIN    CLASS

## Math Focus Points for Discussion

◆ Directly comparing two objects to determine which is longer

Gather students where they can see a tower of ten cubes and a collection of objects so that students can model and explain the strategies they have been using to compare lengths.

## Professional Development

❶ **Dialogue Box:** How Did You Compare?, p. 168

## Teaching Note

❷ **Lining Up Objects for Comparison** Students may have to work with measurement towers for a while before they understand how important it is that objects be lined up at one end in order to compare them accurately. With continued experiences and discussions like these, students will begin to understand the reasons for lining up objects, and using other measurement strategies.

How did you compare your tower to one of these objects? How did you decide whether your tower was longer or shorter?

**Students might say:**

"I stood them on the floor, side by side, to see which one went higher."

Ask students to observe and comment on the strategies their classmates used for comparing and to think about whether they used a similar strategy or a different one.❶

Did anyone else use that strategy? Would someone compare the tower and the [cup] a different way? Can you show us how?❷

*A student shows the class how he lines up an object with his cube tower.*

**SESSION FOLLOW-UP**

## Practice

**Student Math Handbook Flip Chart:** Use the *Student Math Handbook Flip Chart* page 37 to reinforce concepts from today's session. See pages 176–181 in the back of this unit.

# Counting Backwards

## Math Focus Points

◆ Sorting objects into two categories, according to length

◆ Developing strategies for accurately counting and keeping track of quantities up to 12

◆ Counting backwards

### Vocabulary

**counting backwards**
**double-check**

| Today's Plan | | Materials |
|---|---|---|
| **① MATH WORKSHOP**<br>**Counting and Comparing Lengths**<br>**1A Measuring Table**<br>**1B Inventory Bags**<br>**1C Counting Jar** | 🕐 20–30 MIN | **1A** • Materials from Session 2.1, p. 82<br>**1B** • Materials from Session 1.9, p. 65<br>**1C** • Materials from Session 1.8, p. 61 |
| **② DISCUSSION**<br>**Counting Backwards** | 🕐 10 MIN  👥 CLASS | • Counting Jar*<br>• Counting Jar Poster or Booklets |
| **③ SESSION FOLLOW-UP**<br>**Practice** | | • *Student Math Handbook Flip Chart,* pp. 11, 37 |

*See *Materials to Prepare,* p. 77.

## Classroom Routines

*Calendar: What's Missing?* Remove two of the days-of-the-week cards on the monthly calendar. Challenge students to tell you which cards are missing and how they know.

## Math Note

 **Counting Backwards to Double-Check** Counting backwards can be another way of "double-checking" a count. Just as when counting forward, students need to know the rote counting sequence and coordinate this with saying one number for each object. However, when counting backwards, the first number said represents the total amount and each number said next represents the removal of one object.

**MATH WORKSHOP**

# 1 Counting and Comparing Lengths

20–35 MIN

Explain that the following three activities are available during Math Workshop. Remind students what each activity entails, what materials are required, and where they are located.

Ask any students who have not yet visited the Counting Jar to do so today because the discussion at the end of this Session will focus on that activity.

## 1A Measuring Table

 INDIVIDUALS

For complete details about this activity, see Session 2.1, page 84.

**DIFFERENTIATION: Supporting the Range of Learners**

 Students who have sorted all of the objects may enjoy sorting them again against a cube tower of a different length, such as 5 or 15 cubes. What do students notice about how the groups change?

## 1B Inventory Bags

 INDIVIDUALS

For complete details about this activity, see Session 1.9, page 66.

## 1C Counting Jar

 INDIVIDUALS

For complete details about this activity, see Session 1.3, page 40.

**DISCUSSION**

# 2 Counting Backwards

 10 MIN CLASS

## Math Focus Points for Discussion

◆ Counting backwards

Follow your usual routine for discussing the Counting Jar, asking one or two students to model how they counted the objects in the jar. Then, ask:

I'd like us to double-check our count by counting [the objects] in a different way. What will happen if we start with the total number and count backwards as we take them out of the jar. Where do you think we'll land?

Allow students to share their thinking and then try counting backwards together. Direct students' attention to the number line on your Counting Jar poster, to the calendar, or to the Student Math Handbook Flip Chart, so that they can see the number sequence and use it to follow along.

We said there were 10 [objects] in the Jar. Now I am going to take one [object] out and say 9. Why did I say 9?

**Students might say:**

"There were ten pennies, but you took one out, so now there are nine."

*The class counts backwards as the teacher removes objects from the Counting Jar. They use the number line to keep track.*

Continue to take the objects out of the Counting Jar, one at a time, encouraging students to help you count backwards as you do so, until all of the objects are out of the jar. As you remove the last one, you will say, "zero." ❷

SESSION FOLLOW-UP

# ③ Practice

 **Student Math Handbook Flip Chart:** Use the *Student Math Handbook Flip Chart* pages 11, 37 to reinforce concepts from today's session. See pages 176–181 in the back of this unit.

**Teaching Note**

❷ **Practicing Counting Backwards** Continue to find times to count backwards with students so that they become familiar with the number sequence, the relationship between the quantities, and the connection between counting forwards and backwards. Emphasize counting backwards as a way to double-check a set of objects already counted.

# Grab and Count: Compare

## Math Focus Points

◆ Developing strategies for accurately counting and keeping track of quantities up to 12

◆ Comparing two quantities to determine which is more

◆ Developing language for comparing quantities (more, greater, less, fewer, most, least, fewest, same, and equal to)

◆ Directly comparing two objects to determine which is longer

### Vocabulary

more
fewer

| Today's Plan | | | Materials |
|---|---|---|---|
| **1** ACTIVITY<br>**Introducing** *Grab and Count: Compare* | 🕐 5–10 MIN | 👥 CLASS | • M27*<br>• Connecting cubes; coloring materials |
| **2** MATH WORKSHOP<br>**Counting and Comparing Lengths and Quantities**<br>**2A** *Grab and Count: Compare*<br>**2B** Measuring Table<br>**2C** Inventory Bags | 🕐 15–25 MIN | | **2A** • M28 ☑ *<br>• Materials from Activity 1<br>**2B** • Materials from Session 2.1, p. 82<br>**2C** • Materials from Session 1.9, p. 65 |
| **3** DISCUSSION<br>**When It's Hard to Tell** | 🕐 10 MIN | 👥 CLASS | |
| **4** SESSION FOLLOW-UP<br>**Practice** | | | • *Student Math Handbook Flip Chart,* pp. 21–23 |

*See *Materials to Prepare*, p. 77.

## Classroom Routines

*Attendance: How Many Have Counted?* Count around the circle to determine the total number of students present. Pause several times during the count to ask students how many people have counted so far. Help students see why the number they say represents the number of students who have counted so far and that the last number represents the total number of students in class today.

**ACTIVITY**

# Introducing *Grab and Count: Compare*

**5–10 MIN  CLASS**

Gather students around two bins of cubes to introduce this variation of *Grab and Count*. ❶

If I ask [Raul] to grab a handful of these [yellow] cubes, about how many do you think he will be able to grab? What makes you think so? ❷

Set out a pile of five cubes. Then, ask a volunteer to grab a handful of cubes and place them on the floor nearby.

We know this pile has five cubes. About how many cubes do you think there are in the handful [Mia] grabbed? Does it look like five? More than five? Fewer than five? Let's count and find out.

Ask a volunteer to count the cubes, or count them together as a class. Snap them together to make a tower.

Today you're going to compare two handfuls. [Raul] grabbed one handful of [yellow] cubes. Now he's going to grab a handful of [blue] cubes. How many [blue] cubes do you think he will grab?

After the volunteer grabs a second handful, count them and build a second tower. Line up the towers side by side and ask students what they notice. Many students focus first on color. Many kindergarteners are just beginning to think about the concepts of longer and shorter and more and less as attributes. See what students notice on their own first. If students do not talk about one tower having more, prompt them with questions such as these:

Which tower has more cubes? How do you know? Do they have the same number of cubes? Which one has fewer? How do you know?

## Professional Development

❶ **Teacher Note:** *Grab and Count* and Its Variations, p. 161

## Teaching Note

❷ **About How Many?**  Because students have had experience with *Grab and Count,* many will have ideas about what is a reasonable amount to expect a kindergartener to grab. Asking them to think about how many cubes a student may grab engages them in using known information to estimate quantities.

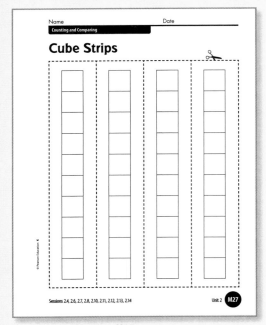

▲ **Resource Masters M27**

If your volunteer grabbed the same amount twice, create another example with towers of different heights. If your volunteer grabbed two different amounts the first time, set up and discuss a second example with towers of the same height.

After discussing two examples, explain how students will record their work. Show the class a pair of Cube Strips (M27) and gather ideas about how they may be used. Explain that, after students have completed their towers, they circle the tower that has more. If the handfuls are the same, students can circle both towers.

*Sample Student Work*

**MATH WORKSHOP**

# ② Counting and Comparing Lengths and Quantities

15–25 MIN

Explain that the following three activities are available during Math Workshop and that today is the last day that both the Measuring Table and Inventory Bags will be available. Remind students what each activity entails, what materials are required, and where they are located.

## 2A *Grab and Count: Compare*

INDIVIDUALS

Students grab two handfuls of connecting cubes. They count and compare the amount in each handful, record their work, and circle the handful that had more.

## ONGOING ASSESSMENT: Observing Students at Work

Students count, represent, and compare quantities.❸

- **How do students count their handfuls?** Do they count accurately, counting each cube once and only once? Do they double-check?

- **How do students compare their handfuls?** Do they compare them visually? Put them side by side to compare them directly? Do they count the number of cubes in each tower? Can they tell which has more and which has fewer? Do they recognize when the towers are of equal height?

- **How do students use the cube strips to record?** Do they color the squares? Cross them out? Label them with letters (e.g., b for blue)? Does their work accurately represent their towers? Do they circle the tower with more?

**Teaching Note**

❸ **Assessing Students as They Compare Quantities** By the end of this unit, students are expected to be able to compare two quantities up to 10 and say which is greater (Benchmark 3). Use Assessment Checklist: Comparing Quantities (M28) to keep track of your observations about students' strategies for comparing two quantities over the course of this Investigation.

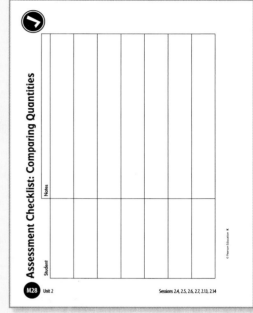

▲ **Resource Masters, M28** ✓

## Assessment Checklist: Comparing Quantities

| Student | Notes |
|---|---|
| Latoya | Grab & Count—Builds towers to see which is taller |
| Jennifer | Grab & Count—makes 2 piles—matches one to one then points out extras = more |
| Kyle | Grab & Count—builds towers "7's more than 5." How do you know? "B/c I looked at the calendar." |
| Hugo (no) | Grab & Count—2 piles—"This is more." How do you know? "I can tell." Can you prove it to me? "Look at them." |
| Lisa (no) | Compare—7 and 8 "Which comes first? Unsure of sequence—suggest use # line & cube towers |
| Raul | Compare: builds towers to see which is taller |
| Yoshio | Names: "Emma's got 4, Corey's got 5—5's more. Look (towers). Corey's got 1 more.". |

### 2B Measuring Table

INDIVIDUALS

For complete details on this activity, see Session 2.1, page 84.

Spend some time with students who are working on this activity today and discuss their work at the end of this session.

### 2C Inventory Bags

INDIVIDUALS

For complete details on this activity, see Session 1.9, page 66.

## DISCUSSION
# ③ When It's Hard to Tell

**10 MIN    CLASS**

### Math Focus Points for Discussion

◆ Directly comparing two objects to determine which is longer

Gather students together to have another discussion about the Measuring Table. Present an object or two that students found difficult to place in either the Longer or Shorter group or objects that different students placed in different categories.

*Some of you put this [picture book] in the group of things that are longer than the tower. Others put the [book] in the other group— things that are shorter than the tower. What do you think about that?*

Share the item in question with the class, and ask students to demonstrate their methods of comparison. Do they notice that many of these hard-to-place objects have one side that is longer and one side that is shorter than the tower? ④ ⑤ ⑥

## SESSION FOLLOW-UP
# ④ Practice

 **Student Math Handbook Flip Chart:** Use the *Student Math Handbook Flip Chart* pages 21–23 to reinforce concepts from today's session. See pages 176–181 in the back of this unit.

---

### Professional Development
④ **Dialogue Box:** You Have to Look at the Long Side, p. 170

---

### Teaching Note
⑤ **Learning to Compare Lengths**  Keep in mind that students learn about comparative measurement by having many opportunities to measure for themselves and to watch others measure. Some students may be unfamiliar with ways to accurately measure and others may understand that comparing in different ways can give different results.

---

### Professional Development
⑥ **Teacher Note:** Learning About Length: Direct Comparison, p. 160

# The Game of Compare

## Math Focus Points

◆ Developing strategies for accurately counting and keeping track of quantities up to 12

◆ Comparing two quantities to determine which is more

◆ Developing language for comparing quantities (more, greater, less, fewer, most, least, fewest, same and equal to)

| Today's Plan | | | Materials |
|---|---|---|---|
| **ACTIVITY** **①** **Introducing the Game of** *Compare* | 5–10 MIN | CLASS | • Primary Number Cards • Connecting cubes |
| **ACTIVITY** **②** **Playing** *Compare* | 15–25 MIN | PAIRS | • Primary Number Cards • Connecting cubes |
| **DISCUSSION** **③** *Compare* | 10 MIN | CLASS | |
| **SESSION FOLLOW-UP** **④** **Homework** | | | • M29–M30, Family Letter* |

*See *Materials to Prepare,* p. 77.

## Classroom Routines

*Today's Question: Which do you like better, rainy days or sunny days?* **On chart paper, create a two-column table entitled "Which do you like better: rainy days or sunny days?" with the label "Rainy Days" at the bottom on one column and "Sunny Days" at the bottom of the other. Have students write their names above the appropriate label. Count the responses as a class. After counting, have a short discussion about the results of the survey.**

## ACTIVITY

5–10 MIN  CLASS

# 1 Introducing the Game of *Compare*

Gather students so that they can see the Primary Number Cards. Choose a student to play a demonstration game with you (or have two students play together).

The object of this game is to decide which of two cards shows more. Each player starts with half the cards in the deck.

Demonstrate how to deal out the cards evenly between the two players, using a "one for you, one for me" strategy. Explain that players sit next to each other so that neither is looking at cards upside down. Players stack their cards facedown, and then both turn over their top card.

*In the game of* Compare, *partners each flip over one card and then decide which card shows the larger number.*

[Yoshio] turned over 6, and [Brad] turned over 4. Which is more? How do you know?

**Students might say:**

"Six is bigger because it comes after 4 when you count."

How else could we figure out who has more?

**Students might say:**

"Count the pictures."

"Build a tower for each number and see which is taller."

Those are all good ideas for figuring out which card shows more. In the game of *Compare,* the person whose card has more says "me." Would [Yoshio] or [Brad] say "me"?

Explain what happens if players turn over the same number.

Sometimes both players turn over the same number. When that happens, both players turn over the next card, and the person with the card that has a greater number says "me."

Explain that the game is over when players have turned over all their cards. Play two or three more rounds until you think students understand the game. If the zero card has not come up in the demonstration, talk with students about what it means.

### ACTIVITY

## 2 Playing *Compare*

15–25 MIN  PAIRS

Pairs play *Compare.* Each player turns over a card. The person with the greater number says, "me." Play continues until there are no cards left.

### ONGOING ASSESSMENT: Observing Students at Work

Students count and compare numbers up to 10.

- **Can students read and interpret the numerals on the cards, or do they count the objects on the cards to figure out the number?**

- **Can students count the objects on the card accurately?** If some students are having difficulty distinguishing 6 from 9, remind them to count the objects on the cards to check and to orient the cards so that the number is on the top.

- **What strategies do students have for determining which number is greater?** Do they just "know"? Do they count objects on the card? Do they use connecting cubes?

- **Do any students use the Ten-Frame arrangement of the objects on the cards to help them quickly determine the quantity (e.g., by counting on from five or back from ten)?**

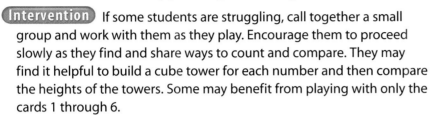

## DIFFERENTIATION: Supporting the Range of Learners

**Intervention** If some students are struggling, call together a small group and work with them as they play. Encourage them to proceed slowly as they find and share ways to count and compare. They may find it helpful to build a cube tower for each number and then compare the heights of the towers. Some may benefit from playing with only the cards 1 through 6.

**DISCUSSION**

**3** *Compare*

10 MIN    CLASS

## Math Focus Points for Discussion

◆ Comparing two quantities to determine which is more

The first few times students play a game in partners, there are some typical problems to watch for. Take a few minutes, as needed, to discuss any that came up. For example, some students sit across from (rather than next to) each other, so that both players are looking at their partner's cards upside down. Other common topics include the following:

- Dealing the cards evenly

- Noise level

- Staying on task/using time productively

- Being a good partner

- Being a good sport (not cheering or gloating when your number is bigger, not getting upset when your number is smaller)

- Being helpful (helping your partner figure out how many are on the card or how to compare the two numbers, but not doing the work for him or her)

- Taking turns

**Dialogue Box:** Playing *Compare* with a Partner, p. 172

Some teachers act out (or role-play) with a student volunteer a problem they have seen, and have the class brainstorm solutions.

If there is time, pose a question or two based on the mathematics of the game. For example, deal a sample hand of two cards, oriented so that all students can see them. You may draw large replicas on chart paper or display transparencies of the two cards on the overhead projector.

This is one round of *Compare* I saw as I walked around the classroom. One player turned over [4], and the other turned over [6]. How did you figure out which card shows more?

**SESSION FOLLOW-UP**

# Homework

**Family Letter:** Send home copies of Family Letter (M29–M30).

# Comparing Two Inventory Bags

## Math Focus Points

◈ Developing strategies for accurately counting and keeping track of quantities up to 12

◈ Comparing two quantities to determine which is more

◈ Directly comparing two objects to determine which is longer

| Today's Plan | | Materials |
|---|---|---|
| **ACTIVITY** ① **Introducing the Longer/Shorter Hunt** | 🕐 5 MIN 👥 CLASS | • Tower of 10 cubes |
| **MATH WORKSHOP** ② **Comparing Lengths and Quantities** ②A Longer/Shorter Hunt ②B *Compare* ②C *Grab and Count: Compare* | 🕐 15–30 MIN | ②A • Towers of 10 cubes ②B • Materials from Session 2.5, p. 100 ②C • Materials from Session 2.4, p. 94 |
| **DISCUSSION** ③ **Comparing Two Inventory Bags** | 🕐 10 MIN 👥 CLASS | • Two Inventory Bags (from Session 1.9, p. 65) |
| **SESSION FOLLOW-UP** ④ **Practice** | | • *Student Handbook Flip Chart,* pp. 21–23 |

## Classroom Routines

*Calendar: Days of the Week*  Use the calendar to review the days of the week, noting which days are school days and which are weekend (or nonschool) days.

# 1 Introducing the Longer/Shorter Hunt

Explain that today there will be a new Math Workshop activity that is very similar to the work students have been doing at the Measuring Table. Instead of comparing their towers of 10 cubes to only the items on the Measuring Table, students go on a Longer/Shorter Hunt, finding things in the classroom that are longer and shorter than their tower of 10 cubes.

Designate two tables (or counters or box tops) as places for items that are "Longer Than My Tower" and "Shorter Than My Tower." Students should find several items to place in each group.

Objects that could be placed in either category depending on the dimension, such as a book or box, make good subjects for discussion.

*Students search for classroom objects that are longer and shorter than a tower of 10 cubes.*

# 2 Comparing Lengths and Quantities

Explain that the following three activities are available during Math Workshop. Remind students of what each activity entails, what materials are required, and where they are located.

## 2A Longer/Shorter Hunt

Students hunt for objects in their classroom that are longer and shorter than their tower of 10 cubes.

## ONGOING ASSESSMENT: Observing Students at Work

Students directly compare a tower of 10 cubes to classroom objects to see which are longer and shorter.

- **How do students compare objects to a tower of 10 cubes?** Do they stand them next to each other? Lay them side by side? Do they align them at one end? Are there some objects students do not need to compare to their tower? How do they handle objects that have one dimension close to the same length as their tower?

- **How do students explain their reasoning?** Do they use vocabulary such as "longer than" and "shorter than"?

## DIFFERENTIATION: Supporting the Range of Learners

**Extension** Some students may enjoy recording what they find out. Fold a blank sheet of paper in half, lengthwise. Write "Longer than my tower" at the top of one column and "Shorter than my tower" at the top of the other. Students can draw pictures of the objects they find, and/or try to write the words.

## 2B *Compare*

**PAIRS**

For complete details about this activity, see Session 2.5, page 101.

## DIFFERENTIATION: Supporting the Range of Learners

**Extension** Variations include the following:

- The player who turns over the card with the smaller number says "me."

- Play with three people and compare three numbers for each round. The player who turns over the card with the greatest number says "me."

## 2C *Grab and Count: Compare*

**INDIVIDUALS**

For complete details about this activity, see Session 2.4, page 95.

## DIFFERENTIATION: Supporting the Range of Learners

**Extension** Students who are ready for more challenge can work in groups of three or four. Each student grabs a handful of cubes and builds a tower. Then, they compare the towers, thinking about questions such as these: Which tower had the most? The least? Did any have the same? How do you know?

## Math Note

❶ **Comparing Different-Sized Objects** Over the last few sessions, students have been comparing quantities. However, because they are comparing different numbers of same-sized objects, students can simply compare the length (or height) of the towers in *Grab and Count* or the rows of pictures in the game of *Compare*. This discussion, which is based on the familiar context of Inventory Bags, challenges students to compare two quantities that *cannot* be accurately compared by looking at length.

DISCUSSION

# ③ Comparing Two Inventory Bags

10 MIN    CLASS

## Math Focus Points for Discussion

◆ Comparing two quantities to determine which is more

Choose two Inventory Bags—one with a smaller number of larger or longer items (e.g., six pencils) and another with a larger number of smaller items (e.g., nine teddy bear counters).❶

I have two of our Inventory Bags here. This one has [pencils] and this one has [teddy bear counters]. How could we find out which bag has more?

### Students might say:

 "We could count the [pencils] and the [teddy bear counters] and see."

 "Pair them up and see which has extras."

 "Line them up and see which is longer."

Focus first on counting the items in each group. Model a particular counting strategy, one some of your students are likely to have been using.

[Sarah] said we could count them. Let's do that. I am going to use a counting strategy that I've seen [Jae] using. [Jae] lines up the things he needs to count and then he counts them. Why do you think he does that?

Take students' suggestions as you make two lines, one of the objects in one of the Inventory Bags, and one of the objects in the other Inventory Bag.

**Teacher Note:** Counting Is More Than 1, 2, 3, p. 151

So here are the [pencils] that were in Bag A, and here are the [teddy bear counters] that were in Bag B. Let's make a prediction. What do you think, are there more [pencils] or [teddy bear counters]?

Some students see the problem in terms of quantities. Others see the length of the line of objects, and think there are more pencils. Clarify for students the question that you are asking. Some students will predict that there are more pencils because they take up more space length wise than the teddy bears.

[Victor] said the line of [pencils] is longer than the line of [teddy bears]. Raise your hand if you agree with [him]. . . . My question, though, is about the *number* of [pencils] and the *number* of [teddy bears]. Which group do you think has more items in it?

Note that for some, the issue is not the way the question is worded or interpreted. These students do not yet conserve quantities—they do not understand that six is always six, no matter what the arrangement. Conservation is a developmental milestone that students reach as they mature.

End by asking a few volunteers to model counting both sets of objects.

So we agree now that there are six [pencils] and nine [teddy bear counters]. Are there more [pencils]? Or more [teddy bear counters]? How do you know?

### SESSION FOLLOW-UP
## Practice

**Student Math Handbook Flip Chart:** Use the *Student Math Handbook Flip Chart* pages 21–23 to reinforce concepts from today's session. See pages 176–181 in the back of this unit.

# Letters in Our Names

## Math Focus Points

◆ Developing strategies for accurately counting and keeping track of quantities up to 12

◆ Creating an equivalent set

◆ Comparing two lengths (or quantities) to see which is longer (or more)

| Today's Plan | | | Materials |
|---|---|---|---|
| **ACTIVITY** ❶ **A Story About a Very Long Name** | 🕐 10 MIN | 👥 CLASS | • A book about a character with a very long name* |
| **ACTIVITY** ❷ **Introducing Making Name Towers** | 🕐 5–10 MIN | 👥 CLASS | • Name cards*; connecting cubes (sorted by color); dot stickers* |
| **MATH WORKSHOP** ❸ **Making Names, Comparing Lengths, Quantities, and Numbers** <br> ❸Ⓐ Making Name Towers <br> ❸Ⓑ Longer/Shorter Hunt <br> ❸Ⓒ *Compare* <br> ❸Ⓓ *Grab and Count: Compare* | 🕐 10–20 MIN | | **3A** • Name cards; connecting cubes (sorted by color); dot stickers <br> **3B** • Materials from Session 2.6, p. 105 <br> **3C** • Materials from Session 2.5, p. 100 <br> **3D** • Materials from Session 2.4, p. 94 |
| **DISCUSSION** ❹ **Checking In** | 🕐 5 MIN | 👥 CLASS | |
| **SESSION FOLLOW-UP** ❺ **Practice** | | | • *Student Activity Book*, p. 11 |

*See *Materials to Prepare*, p. 79.

## Classroom Routines

*Attendance: What If We Start With . . . ?* Count around the circle to determine the total number of students present today. Ask students what they think will happen if the count starts with a different student and why. Choose a different student to start the count and discuss what happened.

**ACTIVITY**

# A Story About a Very Long Name

**10 MIN    CLASS**

Choose a book about a character with a very long name and read it aloud to your students. Then, discuss the length of the main character's name.

[Chrysanthemum, Rumplestiltskin] is a very long name! How many letters do you think are in that name? How could we find out?

Encourage students to share strategies for finding out how many letters are in the character's name.

**Students might say:**

"Let's check the book—it told us how many letters."

"We can count the letters on the cover of the book."

"We could write the name and then count the letters."

Verify the number of letters by testing each strategy that students suggest.

[Lionel] said to look for the page that told us how many letters. We looked and it said that [Chrysanthemum] has [13] letters in it. [Tammy] said we should count the letters in the name on the cover of the book. We did that, and we got [13] again. [Emma] thinks we should write the name and count the letters. [Write the name on the board.] How many letters do you think there are?

Some students realize that, no matter how the name looks, it is the same name with the same number of letters. Others may think that because the name written on the board looks so much longer, it must have more letters. As a group, count the letters in the name again to double-check.

**ACTIVITY**

5–10 MIN  CLASS

# ② Introducing Making Name Towers

If I asked how many letters are in your name, how would you figure that out?

**Students might say:**

"I would write my name down on a piece of paper and count the letters."

"I would look for my name on the wall and count the letters there."

"I would try to spell my name out loud and count the letters as I say them."

After students share their ideas, show them the class set of name cards.❶

Today there is going to be a new Math Workshop activity. The first thing you need to do is to figure out how many letters there are in your name.

Explain that students can use any of the ideas they just talked about and that they can use the name card to double-check.

Once you figure out how many letters are in your name, then you are going to build a cube tower with one cube for each letter.

Use your name, or the name of a child who is absent, to demonstrate.

I have a name card here. How many letters are in [Emma]'s name? How many cubes do we need to make a name tower for [Emma]? How do you know?

Model taking one cube for each letter.

So that we'll know this is [Emma]'s name tower, we are going to label it with her name. If I use one sticker for each letter, how many stickers will I need?

Emphasize using one sticker per cube. Some students understand that the number of letters, cubes, and stickers is the same, but many kindergarten students are still making sense of this idea.

Show students how to label the cube tower with dot stickers.

What is the first letter in [Emma]'s name? How do you know? Can someone find me a sticker that has the letter [E]? I'm going to put the first letter of [Emma]'s name on the first cube. What's the second letter in [Emma]'s name?

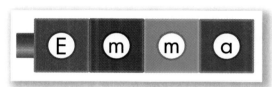

Continue until you have completed the name tower. Count the number of cubes and the number of letter stickers and confirm that they are the same. End by explaining that, during Math Workshop, students will be making their own name towers.

---

**MATH WORKSHOP**

10–20 MIN

# 3 Making Names, Comparing Lengths, Quantities, and Numbers

Explain that the following four activities are available during Math Workshop. Remind students what each activity entails, what materials are required, and where they are located.

## 3A Making Name Towers

INDIVIDUALS

Students figure out how many letters are in their name and use cubes to make name towers with one cube for each letter in their name.

❷ **Storing Name Towers** Explain that students will use their name towers to explore the length of everyone's name during an upcoming Math Workshop activity. Designate a space or container, such as a tray, for storing completed name towers until then.

## ONGOING ASSESSMENT: Observing Students at Work

Students use one-to-one correspondence as they count the letters in their name and then make a cube tower for their name.

- **How do students figure out how many letters are in their name?** Do they write their name and then count? Count the letters on the name card? Count on their fingers as they spell aloud?

- **How do students build their name tower?** Do they count out the total number of cubes? Do they take one cube for each letter as they spell it or match cubes to each letter on their name card? Do they assemble the tower and then add the dot stickers? Do they do the reverse? Do students realize that the number of letters in their name should be the same as the number of cubes and the number of dot stickers they need?

As students finish, ask them to count the number of cubes in their tower, the number of dot stickers they used, and the number of letters in their name to make sure that they match. Encourage pairs of students sitting near each other to compare their towers to see whose name is longer or shorter or whether they are the same length.❷

## DIFFERENTIATION: Supporting the Range of Learners

**Intervention** Rather than counting the letters on their name card some students may try making a cube tower that is the same length as their name on the card.

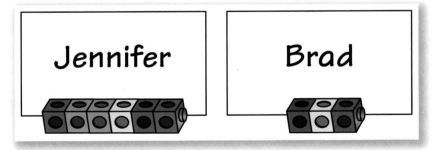

If this happens, ask the student to count the letters on the card and the cubes in the name tower. You may point to the first, the second, and the third letter, and so on, asking the student to show you the cube for each letter. Alternatively, ask about the student's reasoning, but allow the student to discover that there are not enough (or too many) cubes during the process of putting on the lettered dot stickers.

**Extension** Some students may enjoy investigating the number of letters in their middle and last names. Ask them questions such as these: Is your last name longer, shorter, or the same as your first name? What about your middle name? How many total letters are there in your whole name—first, middle, and last?

## 3B Longer/Shorter Hunt

**INDIVIDUALS**

For complete details about this activity, see Session 2.6, page 106.

## DIFFERENTIATION: Supporting the Range of Learners

**Extension** Challenge students who are interested to think about what would happen to their groups if they sorted them again with a cube tower of a different length, such as 5 or 15 cubes. What do students notice about how the groups change?

## 3C *Compare*

**PAIRS**

For complete details about this activity, see Session 2.5, page 101.

## 3D *Grab and Count: Compare*

**INDIVIDUALS**

For complete details on this activity, see Session 2.4, page 95.

**5 MIN** **CLASS**

### DISCUSSION

# 4 Checking In

Take this opportunity to discuss any difficulties that you noticed while observing students at work. The topic may be mathematical in nature, such as a common error or misconception you would like students to discuss (e.g., making a tower as long as the name on the card instead of using one cube for each letter).

The difficulty could also be logistical (e.g., clarifying the steps of the activity or ways to find or attach dot stickers) or management-related (e.g., noise level, working independently and productively).

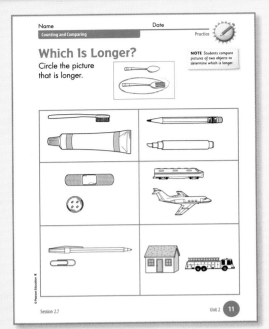

▲ Student Activity Book, p. 11

You may also want to check in to see which students have not yet done this activity and ask those students to begin with this activity tomorrow.

 **SESSION FOLLOW-UP**

# 5 Practice

**Practice:** For reinforcement of this unit's content, have students complete *Student Activity Book* page 11.

# Counting Jar

## Math Focus Points

◆ Developing strategies for accurately counting and keeping track of quantities up to 12

◆ Creating an equivalent set

◆ Comparing two lengths (or quantities) to see which is longer (or more)

| Today's Plan | | Materials |
|---|---|---|
| **ACTIVITY** **1 Introducing the Counting Jar** 5–10 MIN CLASS | | • Counting Jar; name tower*; an index card* |
| **MATH WORKSHOP** **2 Counting and Comparing** **2A** Counting Jar **2B** Making Name Towers **2C** Longer/Shorter Hunt **2D** *Compare* **2E** *Grab and Count: Compare* 20–30 MIN | **2A** **2B** **2C** **2D** **2E** | • Materials from Activity 1 • Materials for the Counting Jar (as you have set it up) • Materials from Session 2.7, p. 110 • Materials from Session 2.6, p. 105 • Materials from Session 2.5, p. 100 • Materials from Session 2.4, p. 94 |
| **DISCUSSION** **3 Checking In** 5 MIN CLASS | | |
| **SESSION FOLLOW-UP** **4 Practice** | | • *Student Math Handbook Flip Chart,* pp. 20, 21–23 |

*See *Materials to Prepare,* p. 79.

## Classroom Routines

*Today's Question: Did you walk or ride to school today?*  On chart paper, create a two-column table entitled "Did you walk or ride to school today?" with the label "Walk" at the bottom of one column and "Ride" at the bottom of the other. Have students write their names above the appropriate label. Count the responses as a class. After counting, have a short discussion about the results of the survey.

**ACTIVITY**

5–10 MIN   CLASS

# 1 Introducing the Counting Jar

Place the prepared name tower you made for the character in the story you read in Session 2.7 in the Counting Jar and show it to students.

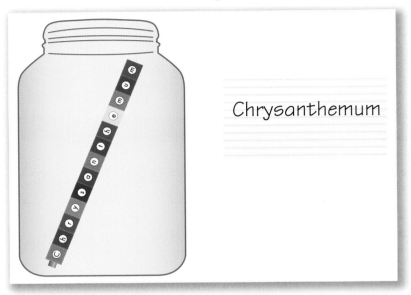

Chrysanthemum

Last week, there were [10 pennies] in the Counting Jar. This week, I put a cube tower in the Counting Jar.

Briefly review the way this activity works in your class, and explain that this will be one of the activities they can choose during Math Workshop over the next few sessions.

Explain that you have written the very long name on an index card. This name card will help students who take apart the tower to count the cubes when reassembling it after they have finished counting.

**MATH WORKSHOP**

20–30 MIN

# 2 Counting and Comparing

Explain that the following five activities are available during Math Workshop and that today is the last day that both *Grab and Count: Compare* and the Longer/Shorter Hunt will be available. Remind students what each activity entails, what materials are required, and where they are located.

All students should finish making a name tower today, because they will need it for the new Math Workshop activity in Session 2.9.

## 2A Counting Jar

**INDIVIDUALS**

Students count the objects in the Counting Jar—a cube tower showing the name of the character in the story you read in Session 2.7. They make a set of the same size and then find a way to record what they found out.

### ONGOING ASSESSMENT: Observing Students at Work

For details on what to observe, see Session 1.3, page 41.

- **Do students recognize that the name tower in the jar represents the character from the story read in Session 2.7?** Do they remember the total number of letters? Do they trust that the tower has that many cubes in it?

### DIFFERENTIATION: Supporting the Range of Learners

**Intervention** Some students may have difficulty counting a set of objects this size. They may not know the sequence of numbers above 10 or may have difficulty keeping track of so many objects. In the first case, count together with students on the number line and then count the cubes together. In the latter, demonstrate touching each cube as you count it or moving each cube to an "already counted" pile as they count it.

## 2B Making Name Towers

**INDIVIDUALS**

For complete details on this activity, see Session 2.7, page 112.

## 2C Longer/Shorter Hunt

**INDIVIDUALS**

For complete details on this activity, see Session 2.6, page 106. After this session ends, and before the discussion at the end of Session 2.9, visit the two areas you have set up for objects that are longer and shorter than students' towers. Choose several objects from each set to present to the class. Mix up several objects on purpose, trading them from one category to the other.

## 2D *Compare*

**PAIRS**

For complete details on this activity, see Session 2.5, page 101.

## 2E *Grab and Count: Compare*

**INDIVIDUALS**

For complete details on this activity, see Session 2.4, page 95.

**DISCUSSION**

# 3 Checking In

**5 MIN   CLASS**

Take this opportunity to discuss any difficulties that you noticed while observing students at work. The topic may be mathematical in nature, such as a strategy you would like all students to consider (e.g., keeping track of a count by moving each object as it is counted) or a common issue you would like students to discuss (e.g., the names and sequence of the numbers over 10).

The difficulty could also be logistical (e.g., clarifying the steps of the activity or discussing what to do if the previous counter took apart the Name Tower) or management-related (e.g., noise level, working independently or with a partner, working productively).

Other alternatives include checking in with students about which activities they have been choosing (e.g., "Thumbs up if you worked on the Counting Jar. Thumbs up if you worked on Making Name Towers.") or allowing students to raise a question or make a comment about that day's math class.

**SESSION FOLLOW-UP**

# 4 Practice

**Student Math Handbook Flip Chart:** Use the *Student Math Handbook Flip Chart* pages 20, 21–23 to reinforce concepts from today's session. See pages 176–181 in the back of this unit.

# Comparing Names

## Math Focus Points

- Comparing two lengths (or quantities) to see which is longer (or more)
- Developing language for comparing lengths (long, longer than, short, shorter than, the same, equal to) and quantities (more, greater, less, fewer, most, least, fewest, same, and equal to)
- Creating an equivalent set

### Vocabulary

same
longer than
shorter than

| Today's Plan | | Materials |
|---|---|---|
| **ACTIVITY** **①** Introducing Comparing Names | 5–10 MIN   CLASS | • *Student Activity Book*, p. 12 <br> • Students' name towers |
| **MATH WORKSHOP** **②** More Counting and Comparing <br> **2A** Comparing Names <br> **2B** Counting Jar <br> **2C** Longer/Shorter Hunt <br> **2D** *Compare* | 15–25 MIN | **2A** • Materials from Activity 1 <br> **2B** • Materials from Session 2.8, p. 117 <br> **2C** • Materials from Session 2.6, p. 105 <br> **2D** • Materials from Session 2.5, p. 100 |
| **DISCUSSION** **③** The Longer/Shorter Hunt | 10 MIN   CLASS | • A subset of the objects students collected during the Longer/Shorter Hunt*; an index card labeled "Longer Than My Tower" and another labeled "Shorter Than My Tower"*; a tower of 10 cubes |
| **SESSION FOLLOW-UP** **④** Practice | | • *Student Math Handbook Flip Chart*, pp. 21–23, 37 |

*See *Materials to Prepare*, p. 79.

## Classroom Routines

*Calendar: How Many Days...?* Students use the calendar to determine how many days until a class event or holiday that will happen this month. Discuss students' strategies for determining the number of days.

### ACTIVITY

# Introducing Comparing Names

5–10 MIN   CLASS

To introduce this activity, select four name towers from your class: one long, one short, and two medium length with the same number of letters.

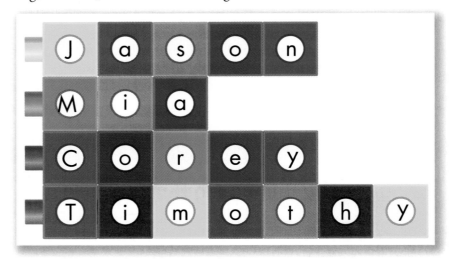

Over the last two days, everyone made a name tower. Today you are going to find names that have more letters than your name, names that have fewer letters, and names with the **same** number of letters.

Hold up one of the medium-length name towers.

Whose name tower is this? . . . [Jason] has 1, 2, 3, 4, 5—5 letters in his name and 5 cubes in his tower. Which of these towers do you think has more letters than [Jason's]? How can you tell?

**Students might say:**

"Stand them next to each other and see which is taller."

Does anyone have a different way to tell?

"Count the cubes to see which has more."

Which tower do you think has fewer letters than [Jason's]? [Kiyo] thinks that [Mia] has fewer letters than [Jason]. Why do you think so?

Again, encourage students to explain and/or demonstrate how they know which name (or tower) has fewer letters (or cubes). Finally, ask students about the last name tower, the one with the same number of letters.

What do you think about [Corey's] tower? How could we compare it with [Jason's]? Do you think it will have more letters? Fewer? The same?

Encourage students to share their thoughts and explain their reasoning.

Explain that, during Math Workshop, students will use the name towers to compare their own name with the names of their classmates.

Show them *Student Activity Book* page 12 and demonstrate how to use it for this activity.

First, you write your name and how many letters are in it. Let's imagine that this is [Jason's] paper. [Write the name and the number of letters in it in the appropriate spaces.] Then, there are two sections—one for names that are shorter than yours [point], and one for names that are longer than yours [point]. Where would [Jason] write [Timothy's] name? [Mia's]?

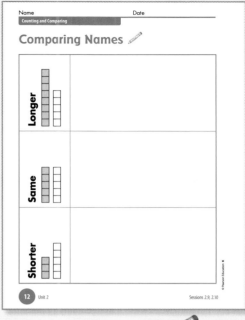

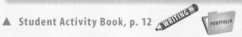

▲ Student Activity Book, p. 12

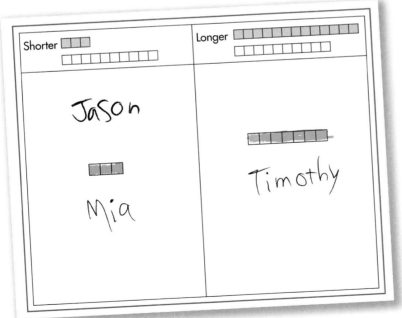

*Sample Student Work*

Remind students that to write each name, they need only copy the letters from the name tower.

## MATH WORKSHOP

15–25 MIN

# 2 More Counting and Comparing

Explain that the following four activities are available during Math Workshop. Remind students what each activity entails, what materials are required, and where they are located.

## 2A Comparing Names

INDIVIDUALS

Students use their individual name towers to compare the lengths of names in the class.

### ONGOING ASSESSMENT: Observing Students at Work

Count and compare quantities (and lengths).

- **How do students compare two towers?** Do they compare them directly? Do they line or stand them up so that one end of each tower is level? Do they count the letters or cubes in the towers and compare the totals? Are there any towers they can place without needing to actually compare them?

- **What language and reasoning do students use to explain how they are comparing names?** How do they explain why they chose to place a name or tower in a particular column?

### DIFFERENTIATION: Supporting the Range of Learners

**Intervention** If there are students who have difficulty with this task, limit the number of name towers they are working with at one time. For example, give students a set of three or four name towers, and ask them to begin by comparing their name tower with just these names.

**Extension** Students with very long or short names record most names in just one section. See whether students discover this on their own. If they do, they may enjoy investigating what happens if they compare a nickname or middle name with the first names of their classmates.

## 2B Counting Jar

INDIVIDUALS

For complete details on this activity, see Session 1.3, page 40.

## 2C Longer/Shorter Hunt

**INDIVIDUALS**

For complete details on this activity, see Session 2.6, page 106.

Remember to choose several objects from the two areas you set up for the Longer/Shorter Hunt before the discussion at the end of this Session. Choose objects that students said were longer than their tower, and several that were shorter than their tower, to present to the class. Also, mix-up several objects on purpose, trading them from one category to the other.

## 2D *Compare*

**PAIRS**

For complete details on this activity, see Session 2.5, page 101.

---

### DISCUSSION
# 3 The Longer/Shorter Hunt

**10 MIN    CLASS**

## Math Focus Points for Discussion

◆ Comparing two lengths to see which is longer

◆ Developing language for comparing lengths (long, longer than, short, shorter than, the same, equal to)

In one area, place the "Longer Than My Tower" index card and several objects that students said were longer than their tower. Also include one or two objects that are *not* longer than a tower of 10 cubes. In another area, place the "Shorter Than My Tower" index card and several objects that students said were shorter than their tower. Also include one or two objects that are *not* shorter than a tower of 10 cubes.

Gather students where they can see the sets of objects and a tower of 10 cubes.

*The class looks over objects in the "Longer Than My Tower" and "Shorter Than My Tower" groups to see whether any have been misplaced.*

For a few days, you were on a Longer/Shorter Hunt. You were looking for objects in our room that were longer than a tower of 10 cubes and objects that were shorter than a tower of 10 cubes. Here are some of the things that you found that were longer than your tower [point to those items]. Here are some of the things you found that were shorter than your tower [point to those items]. Take a minute and look closely at what's in the groups. What do you notice?

Many students quickly notice the objects that are in the wrong category.

**Students might say:**

 "The [crayon] is in the wrong place."

Maybe I got some things mixed up when I moved them from the tables! Can you help me fix them? Why do you think [Sam] thought the [crayon] was in the wrong group?

 "The [crayon] is shorter than 10 cubes, but it's in the "Longer Than" group."

Does anyone see any other objects that seem like they aren't in the right group?

Encourage students to explain why they think an object is placed incorrectly and to use the tower of 10 cubes to prove which category it should go in.

**SESSION FOLLOW-UP**

## Practice

**Student Math Handbook Flip Chart:** Use the *Student Math Handbook Flip Chart* pages 21–23, 37 to reinforce concepts from today's session. See pages 176–181 in the back of this unit.

# Grab and Count: Ordering

## Math Focus Points

◆ Comparing two lengths (or quantities) to see which is longer (or more)

◆ Developing language for comparing lengths (long, longer than, short, shorter than, the same, equal to) and quantities (more, greater, less, fewer, most, least, fewest, same, and equal to)

◆ Creating an equivalent set

<table>
<tr><td colspan="2">**Vocabulary**</td></tr>
<tr><td>most</td><td>smallest</td></tr>
<tr><td>equal</td><td>biggest</td></tr>
<tr><td>fewest</td><td>shortest</td></tr>
<tr><td>in order</td><td>longest</td></tr>
</table>

## Today's Plan | Materials

| Today's Plan | | Materials |
|---|---|---|
| **ACTIVITY**<br>**① Introducing Grab and Count: Ordering** |  5 MIN  CLASS | • M27*<br>• Connecting cubes, sorted by color; coloring materials that match the colors of the cubes |
| **MATH WORKSHOP**<br>**② Counting, Comparing, and Ordering**<br>**2A** *Grab and Count: Ordering*<br>**2B** Comparing Names<br>**2C** Counting Jar<br>**2D** *Compare* |  20–30 MIN | **2A** • Materials from Activity 1<br>**2B** • Materials from Session 2.9, p. 121<br>**2C** • Materials from Session 2.8, p. 117<br>**2D** • Materials from Session 2.5, p. 100 |
| **DISCUSSION**<br>**③ Why Does Mia Have No Names in the Shorter Column?** |  10 MIN  CLASS | • *Student Activity Book*, p. 12 (from Session 2.9) |
| **SESSION FOLLOW-UP**<br>**④ Practice and Homework** | | • *Student Activity Book*, p. 13<br>• *Student Math Handbook Flip Chart*, p. 24 |

*See *Materials to Prepare*, p. 79.

## Classroom Routines

*Attendance: How Many Have Counted?* **Count around the circle to determine the total number of students present. Pause several times during the count to ask students how many people have counted so far. Help students see why the number they say represents the number of students who have counted so far and that the last number represents the total number of students in class today.**

## ACTIVITY

# ① Introducing *Grab and Count: Ordering*

**5 MIN    CLASS**

Explain that today students will be doing another version of *Grab and Count*. Ask four volunteers to each grab a handful of cubes of one color, count them, and build a tower with them. Ask the class what they notice about the four towers. If necessary, prompt them with questions such as these:

Which tower has the most cubes? How do you know? Do any have the same number of cubes? Are any equal? Which tower has the fewest cubes? How do you know?

Then, ask the class to help you put the towers in order.①

What does it mean to put a group of things in order? . . . What if I wanted to put these towers in order from the smallest handful to the biggest handful? How might I do it? What would you do first?②

## Students might say:

"Start with the smallest tower."

"Put towers that are the same size together."

When students agree on how to order the towers, show them the cube strips and demonstrate how to record. Record each handful on a single strip. Put the paper strips in order, and then tape or glue them to a sheet of unlined paper.

Explain that, although four students each grabbed one handful to introduce the activity, during Math Workshop each student will grab four handfuls, order them, and record their work.

### Professional Development

① **Dialogue Box:** Comparing and Ordering Towers, p. 174

### Differentiation

② **English Language Learners** English Language Learners must understand the superlative form *(smallest, biggest)* in order to understand this demonstration. If students seem confused, work with students one-on-one or with a small group of English Language Learners during Math Workshop, emphasizing the words *smallest, biggest,* and *in order.* Encourage students to repeat the words after you.

**MATH WORKSHOP**

20–30 MIN

# Counting, Comparing, and Ordering

Explain that the following four activities are available during Math Workshop. Remind students what each activity entails, what materials are required, and where they are located.

Students need to finish Comparing Names in order to participate in the discussion at the end of this Session.

## 2A Grab and Count: Ordering

INDIVIDUALS   PAIRS

Students grab four separate handfuls of cubes. They build a tower for each and then put them in order from fewest to most.

---

**ONGOING ASSESSMENT: Observing Students at Work**

Students count and compare as they put quantities in order from fewest to most.

- **How do students order a set of cube towers?** Do they attend to the number of cubes in the tower or do they compare only the length or height of the towers? Is their work accurate?

---

**DIFFERENTIATION: Supporting the Range of Learners**

(Intervention) Vary the level of challenge as needed by asking students to order fewer (or more) towers. For example, if students are struggling, ask them first to compare two towers to see which is longer. Then, ask them to choose a third tower and determine where it should go.

## 2B Comparing Names

INDIVIDUALS

For complete details on this activity, see Session 2.9, page 122.

## 2C Counting Jar

INDIVIDUALS

For complete details on this activity, see Session 1.3, page 40.

## 2D Compare

PAIRS

For complete details on this activity, see Session 2.5, page 101.

10 MIN    CLASS

### DISCUSSION

## 3 Why Does Mia Have No Names in the Shorter Column?

### Math Focus Points for Discussion

◆ Comparing two lengths (or quantities) to see which is longer (or more)

◆ Developing language for comparing lengths (long, longer than, short, shorter than, the same, equal to) and quantities (more, greater, less, fewer, most, least, fewest, same, and equal to)

Students need a completed copy of *Student Activity Book* page 12. Begin by asking students to hold up their work.

Take a minute to look around at what your neighbors' paper looks like. What do you notice? Do you see anything interesting?

Allow students to share their thoughts. Most students notice sheets that have a column that is entirely empty. If this does not arise, bring it up yourself:

[Mary] noticed that [Mia] doesn't have any names in the [shorter or longer] column. Why do you think that is? Maybe [Mia] didn't get a chance to finish . . . ? [Mia] said she did finish. So why do you think there are no names in her shorter category?

**Students might say:**

"Maybe [Mia's] name is the shortest name in our class."

After discussing the shortest name(s) in your class, discuss the longest. Use this discussion to introduce the terms shortest and longest. Note whether students use the discussion about the shortest name as they discuss the longest.

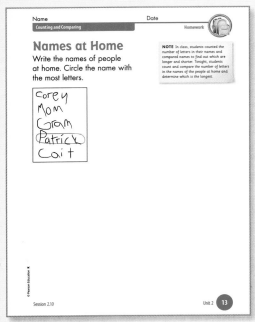

▲ Student Activity Book, p. 13

### SESSION FOLLOW-UP

# Practice and Homework

**Homework:** After comparing the names of the people in their class, students are often interested in counting the letters in the names of the people in their families. Whose name has the most letters? Whose has the fewest? Some may want to put all the names in order by length. Send home *Student Activity Book* page 13 to provide directions. Plan some class time for sharing the results.

*Sample Student Work*

**Student Math Handbook Flip Chart:** Use the *Student Math Handbook Flip Chart* page 24 to reinforce concepts from today's session. See pages 176–181 in the back of this unit.

# Ordering Names

## Math Focus Points

◆ Comparing two (or more) quantities to determine which is more

◆ Ordering quantities from least to most

◆ Developing language for comparing quantities (more, greater, less, fewer, most, least, fewest, same, and equal to)

| Today's Plan | | Materials |
|---|---|---|
| **ACTIVITY** **①** **Introducing Ordering Names** | ⏱ 5–10 MIN 👥 CLASS | • *Student Activity Book,* p. 15 • Students' name towers |
| **MATH WORKSHOP** **②** **Comparing and Ordering** **2A** Ordering Names **2B** *Grab and Count: Ordering* **2C** *Compare* | ⏱ 20–30 MIN | **2A** • Materials from Activity 1 **2B** • Materials from Session 2.10, p. 128 **2C** • Materials from Session 2.5, p. 100 |
| **DISCUSSION** **③** **Checking In** | ⏱ 5 MIN 👥 CLASS | |
| **SESSION FOLLOW-UP** **④** **Practice** | | • *Student Math Handbook Flip Chart,* p. 24 |

## Classroom Routines

*Today's Question: Which color do you like better, red or blue?* On chart paper, create a two-column table entitled "Which color do you like better, red or blue?" with the label "Red" at the bottom of one column and "Blue" at the bottom of the other. Have students write their names above the appropriate label. Count the responses as a class. After counting, have a short discussion about the results of the survey.

# Introducing Ordering Names

Choose four name towers from your class set—one longer name, one shorter name, and two medium names of different lengths. Gather students so that they can see the name towers.

Everyone in our class built a name tower with one cube for each letter. Then everyone spent some time comparing their name to the names of other students in our class. Today we are going to use the name towers in a new way.

Explain to students that they will work with a partner to choose four names of different lengths from the class group of names. They will then compare the number of letters in each of the four names so that they can order them from fewest to most.

Show students the four towers you have chosen and ask them to help you order the towers you have chosen and to explain their reasoning.

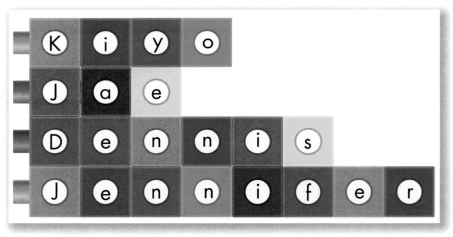

[Beth] said that [Jennifer's] name is the longest. Why do you think so?

**Students might say:**

"Her tower is the tallest."

[Hugo] said that he knows [Kiyo] has more letters than [Jae]. How do you think he knew that?

"Jae's tower is shorter than Kiyo's tower. Jae has 3 and Kiyo has 4."

After you have ordered the towers, show students *Student Activity Book* page 15, Ordering Names, and model how to record for the names you have just ordered.

Pick 4 name towers. Put them in order.
Record your work.

Jae
Kiyo
Dennis
Jennifer

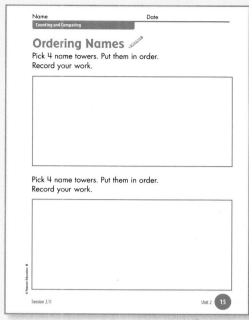

▲ Student Activity Book, p. 15

**MATH WORKSHOP**

**20–30 MIN**

## 2 Comparing and Ordering

Explain that the following three activities are available during Math Workshop. Remind students what each activity entails, what materials are required, and where they are located.

**PAIRS**

### 2A Ordering Names

Students choose four name towers and put them in order from fewest letters to most. They record their work on *Student Activity Book* page 15.

**ONGOING ASSESSMENT: Observing Students at Work**

Students count and compare quantities as they put them in order from fewest to most.

- **How do students order a set of name towers?** Do they attend to the number of letters in a given name (or the number of cubes in the tower) or do they compare only the length of the towers? Is their work accurate?

**DIFFERENTIATION: Supporting the Range of Learners**

**Intervention** Vary the level of challenge, as needed, by asking students to order fewer or more name towers. For example, if students are struggling, ask them first to compare two towers to see which is longer. Then, ask them to choose a third tower and determine where it should go.

**INDIVIDUALS**

### 2B Grab and Count: Ordering

For complete details on this activity, see Session 2.10, page 129.

**DIFFERENTIATION: Supporting the Range of Learners**

**Extension** Students who are ready for more challenge can order more handfuls. After their towers are in order, you may also ask them to figure out how to place an additional handful while keeping all of the towers in order.

**PAIRS**

### 2C Compare

For complete details on this activity, see Session 2.5, page 101.

**DISCUSSION**

# Checking In

**5 MIN    CLASS**

Take this opportunity to discuss any difficulties that you noticed while observing students at work. The topic may be mathematical in nature, such as a strategy you would like all students to consider (e.g., using the number line to figure out the order of the numbers) or a common error you would like students to discuss (e.g., skipping or double counting objects, or omitting or repeating numbers, while counting).

The difficulty may be logistical (e.g., clarifying the steps of the activity, or sharing strategies for things like recording) or management-related (e.g., noise level, sharing materials, working independently and productively).

Other alternatives include checking in with students about which activities they worked on today (e.g., "Thumbs up if you worked on Ordering Names. Thumbs up if you worked on *Grab and Count: Ordering*.") or allowing students to raise a question or make a comment about today's math class.

**SESSION FOLLOW-UP**

# Practice

**Student Math Handbook Flip Chart:** Use the *Student Math Handbook Flip Chart* page 24 to reinforce concepts from today's session. See pages 176–181 in the back of this unit.

# Ordering Cards

## Math Focus Points

◆ Comparing two (or more) quantities to determine which is more

◆ Ordering quantities from least to most

◆ Developing language for comparing quantities (more, greater, less, fewer, most, least, fewest, same, and equal to)

| Today's Plan | | Materials |
|---|---|---|
| **1 ACTIVITY**<br>**Introducing Ordering Cards** | 🕐 5–10 MIN  👫 CLASS | • *Student Activity Book*, p. 16<br>• Primary Number Cards (1 deck, with Wild Cards removed) |
| **2 MATH WORKSHOP**<br>**More Ordering and Comparing**<br>**2A** *Ordering Cards*<br>**2B** Ordering Names<br>**2C** *Grab and Count: Ordering*<br>**2D** *Compare* | 🕐 20–30 MIN | **2A** • Materials from Activity 1<br>**2B** • Materials from Session 2.11, p. 133<br>**2C** • Materials from Session 2.10, p. 128<br>**2D** • Materials from Session 2.5, p. 100 |
| **3 DISCUSSION**<br>**Checking In** | 🕐 5 MIN  👫 CLASS | |
| **4 SESSION FOLLOW-UP**<br>**Practice** | | • *Student Math Handbook Flip Chart*, p. 24 |

## Classroom Routines

*Calendar: What's Missing?* Remove two dates on the monthly calendar. Challenge students to tell you which cards are missing and how they know.

**ACTIVITY**

# Introducing *Ordering Cards*

5–10 MIN CLASS

Gather students so that they can see the Primary Number Cards.

Today we're going to learn a new activity called Ordering Cards. It's a lot like Ordering Names.

Introduce the game by playing a demonstration round or two.

You and your partner will work together to play this game. First, you place the deck of Primary Number Cards facedown in front of you. Then you turn over the top four cards.

Then you and your partner work together to figure out which card shows the smallest number, then the next smaller number, then the next smaller number, and then the biggest number.

How could we put these cards in order and check our work?

**Students might say:**

 "Count the pictures on each card."

 "Find those numbers on the number line. That will tell you the order."

 "We could count out loud to see how the numbers go."

Discuss and try out any strategies that are suggested. When there is agreement about the order, show students *Student Activity Book* page 16 and record the four numbers turned over in the sample round in order.

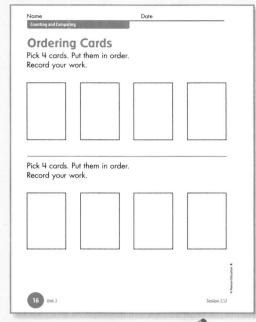

▲ Student Activity Book, p. 16

## MATH WORKSHOP
# More Ordering and Comparing

 20–30 MIN

Explain that the following four activities are available during Math Workshop. Remind students what each activity entails, what materials are required, and where they are located.

 PAIRS

### 2A Ordering Cards

Students put four Primary Number Cards in order from the smallest number to the largest.

### ONGOING ASSESSMENT: Observing Students at Work

Students count and compare to put a set of numbers in order from smallest to largest.

- **How do students decide how to order the numbers?** Do they use the written numbers? Count the objects on the cards? Use classroom tools such as the number line? Do they build cube towers and order them by comparing their length/height? Are they accurate in their work?

- **How do students handle repeat numbers?**

- **How do students record their work?** Do they use numbers?

### DIFFERENTIATION: Supporting the Range of Learners

**Intervention** Adapt the level of difficulty by varying the number of cards students are to order. For example, if students are struggling to order four cards, ask them to compare two. Then introduce a third card and help them determine where it would go.

### 2B Ordering Names

 PAIRS

For complete details on this activity, see Session 2.11, page 134.

### 2C Grab and Count: Ordering

 INDIVIDUALS   PAIRS

For complete details on this activity, see Session 2.10, page 129.

## 2D *Compare*

INDIVIDUALS  PAIRS

For complete details on this activity, see Session 2.5, page 101.

### **3** DISCUSSION
# Checking In

5 MIN  CLASS

Take this opportunity to discuss any difficulties that you noticed while observing students at work. The topic may be mathematical in nature, such as a strategy you would like all students to consider (e.g., using the calendar to figure out the name of a numeral, or the order of several numbers) or a common error or misconception you would like students to discuss.

The difficulty could also be logistical (e.g., clarifying the steps of an activity, or reminding students that the orientation of the cards matters) or management-related (e.g., noise level, working with a partner).

Other alternatives include checking in with students about which activities they worked on (e.g., "Thumbs up if you worked on Ordering Names. Thumbs up if you worked on *Grab and Count: Ordering*."), asking everyone to hold up a piece of work, or allowing students to raise a question or make a comment about today's math class.❶

### **4** SESSION FOLLOW-UP
# Practice

**Student Math Handbook Flip Chart:** Use the *Student Math Handbook Flip Chart* page 24 to reinforce concepts from today's session. See pages 176–181 in the back of this unit.

### Teaching Note

❶ **Preparing for the End-of-Unit Assessment**
Before Session 2.13, gather the Assessment Checklists you have filled in over the course of this unit: Assessment Checklist: Counting (M3), Assessment Checklist: Comparing Lengths (M26), Assessment Checklist: Comparing Quantities (M28). For each benchmark, look over your notes, and sort students into these three categories:
• Those who have clearly met the benchmark,
• Those who have not yet met the benchmark, and
• Those about whom you have questions.

You will be meeting with the students in the latter two categories over the course of Sessions 2.13 and 2.14. You do not need to meet with students who, based on your notes, can consistently count a set of ten objects accurately. Meet only with the students who have not yet demonstrated this skill or have not done so consistently. Make a list of students you need to meet with and specify which tasks you need to do with each student.

| | |
|---|---|
| Brad – | counting 10 |
| Mary – | counting 10 measuring |
| Lisa – | counting 10 comparing to 10 |
| Abby – | measuring |
| Latoya – | measuring |
| Hugo – | comparing to 10 |

# End-of-Unit Assessment and Ordering

## Math Focus Points

◆ Comparing two (or more) quantities to determine which is more

◆ Ordering quantities from least to most

◆ Developing language for comparing quantities (more, greater, less, fewer, most, least, fewest, same, and equal to)

| Today's Plan | | Materials |
|---|---|---|
| **1** MATH WORKSHOP **Comparing, Ordering and Assessment** <br> **1A** End-of-Unit Assessments <br> **1B** *Ordering Cards* <br> **1C** *Ordering Names* <br> **1D** *Grab and Count: Ordering* <br> **1E** *Compare* | 🕐 25–40 MIN | **1A** • Completed and blank copies of M3 ☑ , M26 ☑ , and M28 ☑ * <br> • Connecting cubes; Objects to compare to a tower of 10 cubes*; Primary Number Cards <br> **1B** • Materials from Session 2.12, p. 138 <br> **1C** • Materials from Session 2.11, p. 133 <br> **1D** • Materials from Session 2.10, p. 128 <br> **1E** • Materials from Session 2.5, p. 100 |
| **2** DISCUSSION **Checking In** | 🕐 5 MIN 👥 CLASS | |
| **3** SESSION FOLLOW-UP **Practice** | | • *Student Activity Book,* p. 17 |

*See *Materials to Prepare,* p. 81.

## Classroom Routines

*Attendance: What If We Start With...?* Count around the circle to determine the total number of students present today. Ask students what they think will happen if the count starts with a different student and why. Choose a different student to start the count and discuss what happened.

## MATH WORKSHOP
# Comparing, Ordering, and Assessment

25–40 MIN

Explain that the following four activities are available during Math Workshop. Remind students what each activity entails, what materials are required, and where they are located.

- *Ordering Cards* (See Session 2.12)
- *Ordering Names* (See Session 2.11)
- *Grab and Count: Ordering* (See Session 2.10)
- *Compare* (See Session 2.5)

Explain that, while students are at work on these activities, you will be meeting individually with students. Review any policies you have about such a work time. For example, some teachers have an "ask three before me" rule, which requires that students ask 3 peers before coming to the teacher with a question.

While students are working on these activities, meet individually with those you need to assess.●

**Benchmark 1:** Count a set of up to ten objects

Give students a set of ten loose cubes. Ask them to count them to find out how many there are. Note whether students:

- Know the names and the sequence of the numbers
- Count each object once and only once (which involves having a system for keeping track of what has been counted and what remains to be counted)
- Double-check

When they have finished counting, ask students how many cubes there are. Can students tell you 10 or, do they recount the set to answer the question?

**Benchmark 2:** Decide which of two objects is longer

Ask students to build a tower of 10 cubes. (If they did the counting assessment first, do they know that they already have ten cubes?) Then ask them to compare the tower to the three items you chose (one longer, one shorter, and one with a dimension close to that of a tower of 10 cubes)

● **Whom Do I Need to Meet With?** In order to decide who to meet with individually, gather the Assessment Checklists you have filled in over the course of this unit (M3, M26, and M28). For each benchmark, look over your notes, and sort students into these three categories:
- Those who have clearly met the benchmark.
- Those who have not yet met the benchmark.
- Those you have questions about.

Do the assessment tasks with students in the latter two categories. You do not need to meet with students who, based on your notes, can consistently count a set of 10 objects accurately. Meet only with the students who have not yet demonstrated this skill or have not done so consistently.

| | |
|---|---|
| Brad – | counting 10 |
| Mary – | counting 10 measuring |
| Lisa – | counting 10 comparing to 10 |
| Abby – | measuring |
| Latoya – | measuring |
| Hugo – | comparing to 10 |

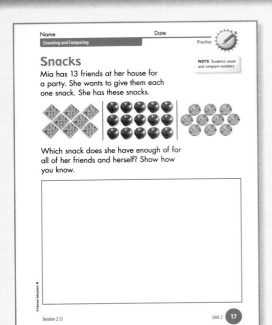

▲ **Student Activity Book, p. 17**

and tell you whether each item is longer than the tower. Note whether students do the following:

- Line up the ends of the objects to compare them

- Hold the tower and the object parallel

- Compare the tower to the longest dimension of the object

**Benchmark 3:** Compare two quantities up to 10 to see which is greater

Explain that you would like to play a few rounds of *Compare.* Flip the top two cards in the deck and ask students to tell you which card has more and how they know. Have cubes available. Note whether students:

- Compare the numbers ("I know eight is more than seven. Look at the calendar.")

- Compare the objects on the cards ("There's one more mitten in this row.")

- Think about one-to-one matching across the two sets

- Build a tower for each number and compare the towers

**DISCUSSION**

# 2 Checking In

5 MIN  CLASS

Take this opportunity to check in with the class. Because you have been meeting individually with students, you may want to discuss any management problems (e.g., noise level, asking a friend before asking the teacher) that arose. You may also want to check in with students about which activities they worked on (e.g., "Thumbs up if you worked on *Ordering Cards.* Thumbs up if you worked on Ordering Names."), or allowing students to raise a question or make a comment about today's math class.

**SESSION FOLLOW-UP**

# 3 Practice

**Practice:** For enrichment, have students complete *Student Activity Book* page 17.

# End-of-Unit Assessment and Ordering Our Names

## Math Focus Points

◆ Comparing two (or more) quantities to determine which is more

◆ Ordering quantities from least to most

◆ Developing language for comparing quantities (more, greater, less, fewer, most, least, fewest, same, and equal to)

| Today's Plan | | Materials |
|---|---|---|
| **MATH WORKSHOP** **① Comparing, Ordering, and Assessment** **1A** End-of-Unit Assessment **1B** *Ordering Cards* **1C** Ordering Names **1D** *Grab and Count: Ordering* **1E** *Compare* | 20–35 MIN | **1A** • Materials from Session 2.13, p. 142 **1B** • Materials from Session 2.12, p. 138 **1C** • Materials from Session 2.11, p. 133 **1D** • Materials from Session 2.10, p. 128 **1E** • Materials from Session 2.5, p. 100 |
| **DISCUSSION** **②  Ordering Our Names** | 10 MIN  CLASS | • Students' name towers |
| **SESSION FOLLOW-UP** **③ Practice** | | • *Student Math Handbook Flip Chart*, pp. 21–23, 24 |

## Classroom Routines

*Today's Question: Are you wearing shoes that tie?* On chart paper, create a two-column table entitled "Are you wearing shoes that tie?" with the label "Yes" at the bottom of one column and "No" at the bottom of the other. Have students write their names above the appropriate label. Count the responses as a class. After counting, have a short discussion about the results of the survey.

20–35 MIN  INDIVIDUALS  PAIRS

**MATH WORKSHOP**

# Comparing, Ordering and Assessment

Explain that the following four activities are available during Math Workshop. Remind students what each activity entails, what materials are required, and where they are located.

- *Ordering Cards* (See Session 2.12.)

- *Ordering Names* (See Session 2.11.)

- *Grab and Count: Ordering* (See Session 2.10.)

- *Compare* (See Session 2.5.)

Explain that, while students are at work on these activities, you will be meeting individually with students.

While students are working on these activities, meet individually with those you need to assess. (See Session 2.13.)①

10 MIN  CLASS

**DISCUSSION**

# Ordering Our Names

## Math Focus Points for Discussion

◆ Ordering quantities from least to most

Gather students so that they can see the complete class set of Name Towers, arranged randomly.

*What if we wanted to put all of the Name Towers in order? I want to make a line that starts with the name with the fewest letters and ends with the name with the most letters. How could we do that?*

**Students might say:**

 "I remember [Mia] and [Jae] were the shortest, and [Mitchell] and [Jennifer] were the longest."

 "Put the names that have the same number of letters together."

 "Make a staircase with them."

Use students' suggestions to build a whole-class representation of the names in your class that goes from fewest letters to most. As you work, occasionally ask students about two particular towers.

Which is shorter? Which is longer? How do you know?

**Students might say:**

 "Line them up side by side. Then you can just see which one is shorter."

Encourage students to show how they would compare towers.

When all of the towers are placed, ask these questions:

What do you notice? What can you tell about our class from looking at all of our name towers in order like this?

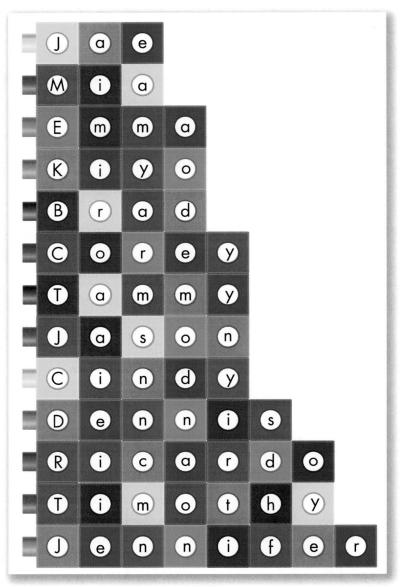

Students are likely to comment on the names that have the fewest and the most letters, and the names that have the same number of letters.

**Students might say:**

"A lot of people have 6 letters in their name."

"Four has the most people."

## DIFFERENTIATION: Supporting the Range of Learners

**Extension** Make a whole-class representation of the number of letters in the names of all the students in your class. This can be a whole-class or small-group activity.

| 3 | 4 | 5 | 6 |
|---|---|---|---|
| J a e | E m m a | C o r e y | D e n n i s |
| M i a | K i y o | T a m m y | L a T o y a |
| | B r a d | J a s o n | |
| | H u g o | C i n d y | |

| 7 | 8 |
|---|---|
| R i c a r d o | J e n n i f e r |
| T i m o t h y | M i t c h e l l |
| R u s s e l l | |

## SESSION FOLLOW-UP

## 3 Practice

**Student Math Handbook Flip Chart:** Use the *Student Math Handbook Flip Chart* pages 21–23, 24 to reinforce concepts from today's session. See pages 176–181 in the back of this unit.

# Professional Development

# Counting and Comparing

In Part 6 of *Implementing Investigations in Kindergarten,* you will find a set of Teacher Notes that addresses topics and issues applicable to the curriculum as a whole rather than to specific curriculum units. They include the following:

Computational Fluency and Place Value

Computation Algorithms and Methods

Representations and Contexts for Mathematical Work

Foundations of Algebra in the Elementary Grades

Discussing Mathematical Ideas

Racial and Linguistic Diversity in the Classroom:
   Raising Questions About What Equity in the Math
   Classroom Means Today

# Counting Is More Than 1, 2, 3

Counting is the basis for understanding our number system and for almost all of the number work in the primary grades. It involves more than just knowing the number names, their sequence, and how to write each number. While it may seem simple, counting is actually quite complex and involves the interplay between a number of skills and concepts.

## Rote Counting

Students need to know the number names and their order by rote; they learn this sequence—both forward and backward—by hearing others count and by counting themselves. However, just as saying the alphabet does not indicate that a student can use written language, being able to say "one, two, three, four, five, six, seven, eight, nine, ten" does not necessarily indicate that students know what those counting words mean. Students also need to use numbers in meaningful ways if they are to build an understanding of quantity and number relationships.

## One-to-One Correspondence

To count accurately, a student must know that one number name stands for one object that is being counted. Often, when young children first begin to count, they do not connect the numbers in the "counting song" to the objects they are counting. Children learn about one-to-one correspondence through repeated opportunities to count sets of objects and to watch others as they count. One-to-one correspondence develops over time with students first counting small groups of objects (up to five or six) accurately, and eventually larger groups.

## Keeping Track

Another important part of counting accurately is being able to keep track of what has already been counted and what remains to be counted. As students first learn to count sets of objects, they often count some objects more than once and skip other objects altogether. Students develop strategies for organizing and keeping track of a count as they realize the need and as they see others use such strategies.

## Connecting Numbers to Quantities

Many young students are still coordinating the ordinal sequence of the numbers with the cardinal meaning of those numbers. In other words, we get to 5 by counting in order 1, 2, 3, 4, 5. Understanding this aspect of number is connected to the one-to-one correspondence between the numbers we say and the objects we are counting. However, being able to count accurately using this ordinal sequence is not the same as knowing that when we have finished counting, the final number in our sequence will tell us the quantity of the things we have counted.

## Conservation

Conservation of number involves understanding that three is always three, whether it is three objects together, three objects spread apart, or some other formation. As students learn to count, you will see many who do not yet understand this idea. They think that the larger the arrangement of objects, the more objects there are. Being able to conserve quantity is not a skill that can be taught; it is a cognitive process that develops as children grow.

## Counting by Groups

Counting a set of objects by equal groups such as 2s, requires that each of the steps mentioned above happens again, at a different level. Students need to know the 2s sequence (2, 4, 6, 8) by rote. They need to realize that one number in this count represents two objects, and that each time they say a number they are adding another group of two to their count. Keeping track while counting by groups becomes a more complex task as well. Students begin to explore counting by groups in the data unit, "Counting Ourselves and Others," as they count the number of eyes in their class. However, most students will not count by groups in a meaningful way until first or second grade.

# Observing Kindergarteners as They Count

In Kindergarten, you can expect to see a wide range of number skills within your class. Students in the same class can vary considerably in age and in their previous experience with numbers and counting.

Your students will have many opportunities to count and use numbers not only in this unit, but throughout the year. You can learn a great deal about what your students understand by observing them. Listen to students as they talk with one another. Observe them as they count orally, as they count objects, and as they use numerals to record. Ask them about their thinking. You may observe some of the following:

## Counting Orally

By the end of the year, most kindergarteners will have learned to rote count to 10 and beyond, with some able to count as high as 100. Many will be able to count orally much higher than they can count objects. Many who have learned the internal counting pattern or sequence (1, 2, 3 . . . 21, 22, 23 . . .), will still find the "bridge" numbers into the next decade (such as 19, 20, or 29, 30) difficult. You may hear children count "twenty-eight, twenty-nine, twenty-ten." Just as the young child who says "I runned away" understands something about the regularities of the English language, the student who says "twenty-ten" understands something about the regularity of the counting numbers. Students gradually learn the bridge numbers as they hear and use the counting sequence.

## Counting Quantities

Most kindergarteners end the year with a grasp of *quantities* up to 20 or so. Some students accurately count quantities above 20, while others may not consistently count smaller quantities. Some may be inconsistent and count successfully one time while having difficulty the next.

Even when students can accurately count the objects in a set, they may not know that the last number counted also describes the number of objects in the set. You may observe students who successfully count a set of cubes, but have to go back and recount the set to answer the question, "How many cubes are there?" These students have not yet connected the counting numbers to the quantity of objects in a set. Students develop their understanding of quantity through repeated experiences organizing and counting sets of objects. In Kindergarten, many of the activities that focus on quantity can be adjusted so that students are working at a level of challenge appropriate for them.

## Organizing a Count

Some students may be able to count objects they can pick up, move around, and organize with far more accuracy than they can when counting static objects, such as pictures of things on a page. You may observe some students who can count objects correctly when the group is organized for them, but you will see others who have trouble organizing or keeping track of objects themselves. They will need many and varied experiences with counting to develop techniques for counting accurately and for keeping track of what they are counting.

## Counting by Writing Numbers

Knowing how to write numerals is not directly related to counting and understanding quantity; however, it is useful for representing a quantity that has been counted. Young students who are learning how to write numerals frequently reverse numbers or digits. Often this is not a mathematical problem but a matter of experience. Students need many opportunities to see how numerals are formed and to practice writing them. They should gain this experience by using numbers to record mathematical information, such as the number of students in school today or the number of objects on a page of a counting book. Numeral formation is related to letter formation; both are important in order to communicate in writing. We recommend that rote practice of numeral writing be part of handwriting instruction rather than mathematics.

# Assessing Students' Counting

By the end of this unit, students are expected to be able to count a set of ten objects accurately (Benchmark 1). This means that they know the number names in sequence, say one number for each object, and have a system for keeping track of what they are counting. Assessment Checklist: Counting (M3) is included to help you keep track of what you observe about students' counting over the course of this Investigation and the unit. (Also see the **Teacher Notes:** Counting Is More Than 1, 2, 3, and Observing Kindergarteners as They Count, pages 151–152, for more information on how students learn to count and on what to look for as you watch students count.) What follows is a vignette from one teacher, describing what she learned about students as she observed their work on Inventory Bags in Session 1.9.

*After introducing the Inventory Bag activity, I circulated among pairs of students to see what strategies they were using to count. I was amazed and somewhat overwhelmed at the variety of different ways students had for counting a group of objects.*

## Counting Pencils

*When I joined Brad and Russell, they were just pouring the pencils from their inventory bag onto the table. They seemed excited to find out what was in the bag. When I asked Brad to count how many pencils there were, he began pointing in the air and saying the number sequence. He seemed to know the sequence quite well (he counted up to 15), but did not seem to attach these words to the objects in the bag.*

*Russell then took a turn counting the pencils. He counted accurately, lining up the pencils and touching each one as he counted it. He paused when he hit ten, looking to me for the name of the next number. Brad said "11" and then Russell announced that he thought there were 12 pencils. Either he didn't remember that Brad had said 15, or that fact didn't bother him.*

## Counting Crayons

*When I joined Cindy, she was hard at work on her representation. The crayons from her Inventory Bag were on the table, sorted by color, and she had made detailed drawings of two blue crayons. I asked how many crayons were in her bag, and she surprised me by answering, "I don't know yet." I realized that she was drawing the crayons one by one. She would put a crayon on her paper, draw it, put it back in the bag, and then take the next crayon from the table to be counted.*

*I revisited Cindy after she completed her picture, which showed a haphazard arrangement of crayons. Cindy had a hard time counting them because they were drawn almost in a circle. Her partner, Dennis, looked up from his own work to suggest that she count one crayon at a time and place them in a line on the table. With his help, Cindy was able to count the crayons.*

## Counting Cubes

*When I joined Mary and Latoya, they had already written "8 cubes" on their papers, using the label on their bag to spell cubes. I asked them to show me how they found out that there were eight.*

*Mary counted the cubes, which were in a pile on the table. She touched the cubes as she counted them but did not move them in any way—they remained in a scattered pile on the table. As she counted, I noticed that she skipped several cubes and recounted several others but managed to end up with eight.*

*Latoya was carefully observing Mary as she counted and looked puzzled. I asked her why. She said, "Well, Mary got eight, and I think it's eight too. But when I watched her count, I thought she counted this cube twice so I didn't think she was going to get eight."*

Mary didn't seem to follow this line of reasoning, even after I rephrased what Latoya had said. I asked Mary to recount. She did, in a similar manner. I asked Latoya if she had a strategy that helped her avoid counting any cubes twice. She demonstrated, moving each cube as she counted it and announced, somewhat relieved, "There really were eight."

## Counting Teddy Bears

Mitchell and Emma's bag contained teddy bear counters of several colors. They sorted the bears into piles of like colors—two purple, three red, four yellow, and two green—and made tallies to show each group. As I watched Mitchell, he got lost in his counting several times. Each time this happened he started again at 1. Even though some of the groups were small and all of the bears were visible, he was unable to look at any of the arrangements and count them in his head or recognize a group without counting them.

When I asked Mitchell how many bears there were altogether, he went back to the groups of bears and counted them, beginning again several times before announcing that there were ten.

His partner, Emma, heard this and recounted her tally marks. I asked her why she did that. Her response was, "Because I counted 11."

I asked what made her to decide to recount. She told me, "Well, Mitchell just said he got ten. And I thought we had 11. We both counted the bears in the bag, so we should have the same number."

## Counting Blocks

Jason and Lisa had a bag of seven blocks from the block center. Jason stacked the blocks into a tower and counted them for me. He did not touch the blocks, but he pointed to them as he said each number.

Lisa tried to mimic Jason's actions, but she repeatedly got lost in the sequence, looking to us for the name of the number that came next or guessing the name of a number she had heard before. ("1, 2, 3 . . . 8?") She would often get further in the sequence if I asked her to start from 1.

## Counting Keys

Hugo was counting keys, which were in a pile on the table. As he counted, he moved the keys from one pile to another. Several times he lost track of where he was, once because he overheard a neighbor's count:

**Hugo:** 5, 6, 7 . . .

**Neighbor:** 9, 10, 11.

**Hugo:** . . . 12, 13.

When Hugo lost track like this, he would push all the keys into one pile and start again from one. He was eventually able to count the group of nine keys accurately, and I was impressed by his ability to stick with the task.

Observing students as they worked on this activity provided me with a wealth of information about their rote knowledge of the sequence of numbers, their strategies for counting and keeping track of a set of objects, and their comfort with recording their mathematical work. With Assessment Checklist: Counting (M3) on a clipboard, I was able to take notes on students' strategies.

# Assessment Checklist: Counting

| Student | Knows the names of the numbers, in order | Counts each object once and only once | Has a system for keeping track | Double-checks | Notes |
|---------|------------------------------------------|---------------------------------------|---------------------------------|----------------|-------|
| Brad | 10/6 ✓ to 15 | No | No (pointing in air) | No | Random pointing—no connection b/t #s & objects → sm GRP |
| Russell | 10/6 ✓ to 10 . . .? given 11. ✓ 12 | ✓ | ✓ (line up & touch) | | Ok w/diff. #s |
| Cindy | 10/6 ✓ to 9 | | Sorts by color but doesn't use. | | Draws 1st, then counts. |
| Mary | 10/6 ✓ to 8 | No. | No, pile | | Counting until she hears the # Latoya said was the answer? → sm GRP, w/Brad. |
| Latoya | 10/6 ✓ to 8 | ✓ | ✓ (moves as counts) | ✓ | Wonders why same # if Mary didn't count accurately. |
| Mitchell | 10/6 ✓ to 10 | Yes, but takes multiple tries. | | ✓ persistent! | Can't "see" 2, 3. Must start from 1 no matter what grp |
| Emma | 10/6 ✓ to 11 | | | ✓ | Expects same total |
| Jason | 10/6 ✓ to 7 | ✓ | ✓ (points) | | |
| Lisa | 10/6 1, 2, 3. . . 8? No. | ? | blocks stacked by Jason | | → Sequence |
| Hugo | 10/6 ✓ to 13 | ✓ | ✓ (moves as counts) | ✓ | Easily distractd by others counting—persistent |

*These notes help me assess where students are, and plan appropriate next experiences for individuals, small groups, and the class as a whole. For example, Russell, Dennis, Latoya, Emma, and Jason seemed to have a strong grasp of the counting sequence and how it relates to a group of objects. Cindy, Mitchell, and Hugo seemed to have a good grasp of the sequence, but needed to develop systems for keeping track of and possibly organizing their counts.*

*I was somewhat surprised and concerned by Brad, Mary, and Lisa. I realized that Lisa needed a lot of practice with the sequence of numbers, and all three students needed a lot of practice counting small quantities to begin to connect the counting sequence to the set of objects. I made a note to myself to visit them individually, so I can assess them more closely and in a small-group format, where they can watch and hear others count and see others' strategies for saying one number for each object.*

*I was also surprised that a handful of students seemed ready to grapple with the issues that arise when different people count the same set of objects and get different numbers.*

This unit provides many opportunities to assess students as they count. Because Inventory Bags comes at the end of Investigation 1, this is a good time to look over the copies of Assessment Checklist: Counting (M3) you have completed so far. Use them to think about whom already meets the benchmark, who is on the cusp, and who needs a lot more experience and practice. While Investigation 2 focuses on measurement by direct comparison and comparing quantities, counting is a big part of many of these activities. Therefore, you can continue to assess the students in the latter two categories, and to model and discuss counting strategies as you do so. Make another copy of Assessment Checklist: Counting (M3) with only these students' names, to remind yourself about who is still working on this idea, and to give yourself a place to keep track of their progress during Investigation 2. (At the end of this unit, you will do another sort, and spend the End-of-Unit Assessment Session with only those students who do not clearly meet the benchmark.)

# Students' Counting Books

Observing students as they work and listening to them explain what they are doing is especially important in Kindergarten when students' written work can be difficult to decipher and understand. In a classroom in which students were making their own counting books similar to *Anno's Counting Book,* the teacher found that her observations of and conversations with students were essential to interpreting their written work.

The teacher provided a variety of materials for students to use in making their books. Rubber stamps and shapes punched from colored paper (to be glued down) offered students an alternative to drawing, which was a difficult task for some.

## Finding an Underlying Order

At first glance, the teacher was concerned about Tammy's work. Her 2 page and 3 page looked chaotic; it was hard to imagine that Tammy had counted correctly. However, upon closer inspection and an explanation from Tammy, the teacher saw that, in fact, Tammy had included many groups of the correct number on each page, often identified by color (two red bears, two green bears, two green rabbits, two blue dinosaurs, and so forth). Her groups were just difficult to recognize because of the scattered placement and the extra decorations.

*Tammy's Work*

## Clarifying a Student's Intent

Hugo used a variety of materials, including rubber stamps (bears, rabbits, and dinosaurs), drawings (surfers and pumpkins), and words (boo and boom) to illustrate his book. He began with a page similar to Anno's first page: his 0 page shows only a river and a bridge. However, this seems to have confused Hugo because when he got to the 1 page, he had already drawn one bridge and now went on to draw two bridges. To add to the confusion on his 1 page, Hugo seemed to be using rubber stamps in groups of three. But this was clarified when the teacher asked him to explain his thinking and Hugo said, "There's one red bear, one red bunny, one red dinosaur. There's one blue bear, one blue bunny. . ."

*Hugo's Work*

*Hugo's Work*

## Correcting an Error

Corey also used a variety of materials to illustrate her book, including colored markers and shapes punched from paper. Her pictures were accurate and clearly organized. However, after illustrating the 6 page, Corey was concerned. She brought her book to the teacher and explained the dilemma —she had accidentally made a group of more than six objects. When asked how she would fix her mistake, Corey had just one idea: crossing out two of the objects, a solution that did not please her. The teacher suggested that Corey could add more things to each group (more cutout shapes to the top group and more hand-drawn hearts below), resulting in two groups of six. Corey was unable to make sense of this idea and decided to cross out two of her hearts, leaving a single group of six mixed objects.

*Corey's Work*

## Interpreting Drawings

For Mitchell, drawing is an arduous task. Because he does not use representational drawings, it is difficult to interpret his work, and at first glance his work may seem inaccurate. But when Mitchell sat down to talk about his book with the teacher, it was clear that the pictures had meaning for him, and he was able to point out the groups that represented the number on each page. In this instance, as in the previous three, a brief conversation helped the teacher assess the student's understanding.

*Mitchell's Work*

# Learning About Length: Direct Comparison

In Kindergarten, students start working with ideas about what is *long, longer, short,* and *shorter.* Their ideas about length begin to develop as they compare lengths directly.

"My sister is taller than I am."

"My pencil is the shortest in the class."

Research on children's mathematical understanding shows that students typically do not develop a firm idea about length as a stable, measurable dimension until second grade, although there is quite a range of individual differences among students.

Students in your class may vary quite a bit in how accurately and consistently they compare the lengths of things. You will probably see some who do not carefully line up objects in order to compare them. You may also see students comparing along a dimension that is not the longest. These *mistakes* are probably not just carelessness or sloppiness; instead, these students are still figuring out what measurement is about.

Rather than simply telling students to carefully align the ends of two objects in order to compare them or demonstrating how to measure with a tower of cubes, encourage discussion among students about different ways they are measuring.

**Teacher:** Some people thought that this box was longer than our cube tower, and some said it was shorter. Who would like to show how you measured this box? Brad lined up his cube tower like this. Do you think that's correct? Why or why not?

At times, you may show students some inaccurate ways of measuring to help them think through and articulate their own ideas. For example, compare the length of a cube tower with a dimension of an object that is clearly not the longest one.

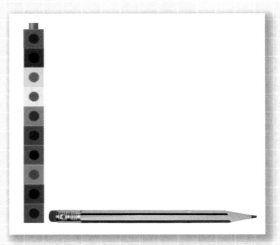

You may also hold the tower in an unusual way to compare the lengths, such as crosswise horizontally or diagonally.

Ask students whether each approach is a good way to compare the lengths of the two objects, and if it is not, what you should do to get a better comparison. As students discuss and compare ways of measuring, they will gradually develop a sense of what length is and how to measure it accurately.

# Grab and Count and Its Variations

*Grab and Count* is an activity that Kindergarten students never seem to tire of. The basic activity and its variations offer repeated experience with counting, comparing, organizing, keeping track of, and representing quantities. This is a good example of how teachers can take a basic activity and, when it is familiar to students, change it in a variety of ways to build on students' previous experiences while also extending the mathematics they are investigating. Because the structure is familiar to them, students can revisit the activity fairly easily and independently. In any of the *Grab and Count* activities, you can vary the size of the objects to be grabbed and thereby adjust the numbers that students will be working with in order to offer different students an appropriate level of challenge.

*This student grabbed a handful of foam peanuts. He traced each one and then counted them, drawing a line under each picture to help him keep track. He then recorded the number 6.*

## Grab and Count

In the basic version of *Grab and Count,* students grab a handful of cubes, count to find out how many they were able to grab, and find their own way to represent their handful on *Grab and Count* (M12).

▲ **Resource Masters, M12**

## Grab and Count: Compare

In this variation, students grab two handfuls of cubes, each of a different color. They count and build towers with the cubes and compare them, thinking about which handful had more and how they knew. Finally, students use two Cube Strips to represent their handfuls, circling the strip with more.

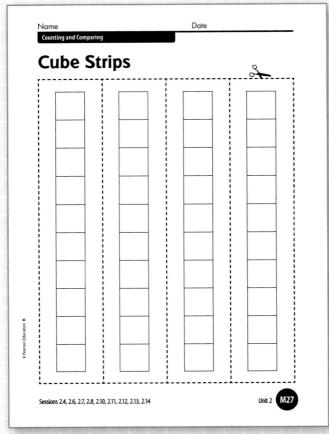

Name _____ Date _____

Counting and Comparing

## Cube Strips

✂

© Pearson Education K

Sessions 2.4, 2.6, 2.7, 2.8, 2.10, 2.11, 2.12, 2.13, 2.14    Unit 2  **M27**

▲ **Resource Masters, M27**

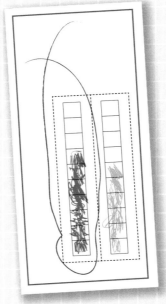

*Sample Student Work*

Students take different approaches to recording their amounts. Some place a cube tower adjacent to the paper cube strip and color corresponding squares. Others lay the tower directly on the strip and remove one cube at a time to color the square beneath it. Still others count the cubes in a tower and then count and color the same number of squares on the strip. None of these approaches is better than the others, and students should be encouraged to find their own recording method.

### Grab and Count: Ordering

In this variation, students grab four handfuls of cubes, each of a different color, and put them in order from fewest to most. Students color in individual cube strips and tape them, in order, onto a sheet of paper.

*Sample Student Work*

### Grab and Count: Two Handfuls

In this variation, introduced in *Counting and Measuring*, students grab two handfuls of cubes and figure out how many they grabbed altogether. They find their own way to represent their handful on *Student Activity Book* page 5.

# What Do We Count and Why?

Before reading a counting book with her students in Session 1.1, the teacher asks students to suggest activities and situations in which people count. The goal of the discussion is to encourage students to think of counting as more than just naming a string of numbers.

**Teacher:** Who has an idea about what it means to count?

**Abby:** Counting is the numbers.

**Mia:** Yeah, like 1, 2, 3, 4, 5.

**Teacher:** Okay, those are the numbers you say when you count. But why do people count? What are they doing when they count?

**Hugo:** At morning meeting we count.

**Raul:** You count all of us. You pick a name and that person starts. You say your number and go around the circle. If you pick my name out, I say, "1" and Jennifer says, "2," and the next person says "3," and then "4."

**Teacher:** Hugo and Raul said we count during attendance. Can anyone think of some other times that we count during the day?

The class brainstorms a list that includes attendance, snack, and calendar.

**Teacher:** Raul said earlier that we count students at attendance time. Why do you think we do that? Why do we need to count the kids in our class?

**Mary:** Because you have to tell the office how many kids are here and how many kids didn't come to school. So they know.

**Teacher:** What about snack time? Carmen said we count at snack time. What do we count at snack? Do we count students?

**Cindy:** We count how many kids want chocolate milk and how many want white milk.

**Rebecca:** When I was snack person, I had to count and give everyone at my table five crackers so everyone has the same.

**Teacher:** So were you counting people?

**Rebecca:** No, I was counting snacks. The crackers.

**Teacher:** Why was it important to count how many crackers?

**Rebecca:** Because it's not fair if someone gets more than everyone else. Or if I messed up and didn't give someone five, they might feel bad cause they didn't get as much as everyone else.

Kindergarteners have many relevant ideas about the importance of counting in everyday situations and interactions. Look for opportunities throughout the school day to count and to highlight your reason for counting.

# Pictures in a Counting Book

In Session 1.1, the class reads a counting book. This teacher chose *Anno's Counting Book* by Mitsumasa Anno. Confusion sometimes arises when students notice that on the page for the number 1, there are two people and two trees. Students grapple with issues of classification as they investigate how the illustrations represent the numeral on the page.

**Teacher:** Jack thinks this is the "1" page. Why do you think Jack thinks that?

**Timothy:** Because one family moved in and there was no one before.

**Mary:** Because there's a 1 here (points to the numeral), and a 1 here on the snowman.

**Manuel:** And one cube, too.

**Jennifer:** It's a counting book. After zero comes one.

**Teacher:** If this is the "1" page, do you see one of anything on this page?

**Jennifer:** There's one tree.

Other students point out that there is one house, one river, one bird, one sun, one snowman, one shovel, and one dog.

**Manuel:** I think it's the "1" page, but . . . I see two trees. And two people, too. See? There's one skiing and there's one by the snowman.

**Teacher:** Interesting! We think this is the "1" page, but Manuel sees two trees (points them out) and two people (points). What do others think about that?

**Timothy:** Well, everything's not one. There's two chimneys and lots of windows . . .

**Jennifer:** I didn't see the other tree. But they look different. They're not the same trees.

**Jack:** I think so, too. It's the same, like there's two animals, but there's one dog and one bird. There's two trees, but they're different.

**Teacher:** What about the people? How are they one?

**Jack:** It's kind of the same thing. There's two people, but one looks like a kid and the other's a grown-up.

**Victor:** Or maybe it's a mom or dad and it's one, one family.

As these students think about how the illustrations on each page represent the numeral on the page, they are beginning to connect numerals with the quantities they represent.

# Does the Order Matter?

After all of her students have had a chance to visit the Counting Jar, which had three red checkers and five black checkers in it, the teacher calls them together to discuss their findings in Session 1.6. She begins by highlighting a particular counting strategy—Emma's organization of the checkers—as a springboard for discussing whether order matters when counting. This is the seed of an idea that students will return to in Grades 1 and 2 when they are working on addition. This same idea will later be formulated as the commutative property of addition.

**Teacher:** When I was watching you at the Counting Jar, I noticed Emma doing something interesting. Emma, would you show us how you organized the checkers to count them? (Emma places the three red checkers in a row above the five black checkers.) Emma, why did you put the checkers in two lines like that?

**Emma:** It makes it easier for me to count them.

The teacher explains that sometimes, when counting a group of objects, it is hard to remember which ones have already been counted and which ones still need to be counted, and that Emma's strategy might help students keep track. Then, she asks a different volunteer to count the checkers. Jason does and gets a total of eight checkers.

**Teacher:** I noticed that when Jason counted, he counted the red ones first and the black ones second. I'm wondering what will happen if we count the black ones first and the red ones second? (The teacher rearranges the checkers so that the row of reds is below the row of blacks. Some children say "nothing," and others say, "the same thing.") The same thing? Carmen why do you think we're going to end up with the same thing if we count them in a different order?

**Carmen:** Because you'll still have all the other ones unless you just take one away.

**Jennifer:** If you take one away, it would change it, but if you didn't, it would be the same.

**Teacher:** Okay, we're still going to have all the other ones unless we take one away. Are we going to take one away? (Carmen responds "No.") No, what are we doing that's different?

**Carmen:** You're doing them in a different order.

**Teacher:** We're doing it in a different order. I have a really important question for you. Do you think it *matters* if we change the order? (Some students say "yes," and others say "no.") What will happen if we count the black checkers first?

**Rebecca:** Nothing.

**Teacher:** Rebecca says nothing. Nothing's going to happen, it's not going to change it. Rebecca, how come nothing will happen?

**Rebecca:** 'Cause it's still eight.

**Teacher:** Okay, it's still eight checkers there.

**Mitchell:** I think you still end up with eight but instead of counting the three first, you count the five first.

**Jae:** I also think you will get eight.

**Teacher:** Why?

**Jae:** I don't know.

**Teacher:** Should we test it and see?

The class says yes. Mia volunteers to count. She touches each checker as she counts, starting with the black and then counting the red checkers. She gets eight.

**Teacher:** What happened?

**Hugo:** Same number. It's always going to be the same number.

**Teacher:** You think it's *always* going to be the same number?

**Lionel:** It doesn't matter what order it is. It all depends on what number it is. It's still going to be eight, 'cause it's the same number.

**Teacher:** Is this getting the same answer no matter which order you counted something special about the checkers, or would it work with anything?

**Sarah:** If you take the same number, it would be the same. (She sets out three yellow and five blue teddy bear counters. She counts the yellows first, then the blues, and gets eight.)

**Teacher:** What if you count the blues first?

**Abby:** Still eight! You can even do this (arranges the teddy bears in a line: yellow, blue, yellow, blue, yellow, blue, blue, blue and counts them) and it's still eight.

**Manuel:** It doesn't matter how you do the colors, it matters how many there are.

When asked whether order matters when counting, some students said yes and others said no. However, the students who participate in this discussion seem certain that when counting a set of objects, the order does not matter. This teacher knows that some of her students, such as Jae, cannot yet explain *why* the order does not matter, and others are not yet sure that it does not. In fact, she is fairly certain that a few students may still believe that eight checkers stretched out in a long line is *more* than eight checkers pushed together in a short line. Because the teacher knows that this range exists in her classroom, she will revisit this idea in various contexts throughout the year to help students develop and deepen their thinking and their ability to explain the concept.

# Dialogue Box

# Is It 10 or 11?

During work with Inventory Bags, situations often arise in which different students count the same collection and arrive at different numbers. This is tricky for a teacher to handle because clearly only one count is right. However, simply verifying which one is right may not improve students' understanding of numbers and counting. In fact, without probing further, you cannot know whether the student with the accurate count does in fact have a better understanding.

When discrepancies arise, focus on strategies for keeping track of a count, reasons for losing count, and ways to double-check. Involve students in thinking about why there may be differences in the count for a particular bag. For example, consider how Ms. E. handles this conversation about Inventory Bags, which took place in Session 1.10.

**Teacher:** Who did an inventory of Bag F?

**Sarah:** Me and Kiyo. We had pencils in our bag and there were 11.

**Corey:** But me and Mia had pencils, and there were 10, not 11.

**Teacher:** Interesting. Two different pairs inventoried this bag. Sarah and Kiyo counted 11 pencils, and Corey and Mia counted 10. What do other folks think about that?

**Tammy:** Maybe some fell out of the bag or got lost.

**Teacher:** That's certainly one reason they could have ended up with different numbers. What if I told you I'm sure that all the pencils were there for both pairs? None were lost and none were added to the bag. Are there any other reasons they might have gotten different numbers? . . .

**Teacher:** I know some of you had a hard time agreeing on how many things were in your bags. Kyle and Raul, I saw you having a similar problem. Can you tell us about what happened with your cube inventory?

**Kyle:** Well, I counted first and got 9 cubes. And then Raul counted them and he got 10.

**Teacher:** Raul, how did you and Kyle work this out?

**Raul:** We both counted the cubes again. And then I got 9 that time.

**Teacher:** So no one took any cubes away, or added any cubes to their pile, but Kyle and Raul still got different numbers. Why do you think that might be?

**Kyle:** Well, one time when I watched, Raul touched a cube two times by mistake. And when I was counting at first I kept getting messed up 'cause I forget which ones I counted and I kept having to start over. Then I snapped them together as I said the number and counted them that way. Then I got 9 two times in a row and so did Raul.

**Teacher:** So it sounds like snapping them together as you counted helped you keep track of the cubes, and that double-checking helped you make sure that there really were 9, not 10 or 8.

The teacher then returned the discussion to the bag of pencils, asking students for ways the two pairs could check their results.

You can reassure students that, in fact, it is quite easy for anyone to be off by one or two in a count. It is a familiar experience for most of us to recount something and get a different number. Students should understand that although it is easy to miscount, there are strategies that help us be sure of our result. These include recounting ourselves, asking someone else to count to double-check, and carefully touching each object or moving it from one spot to another as we say each successive number.

# Dialogue Box

# How Did You Compare?

This class has been working at the Measuring Table, sorting a set of objects into two groups: longer than my tower and shorter than my tower. In Session 2.2, students are gathered to discuss the strategies they have been using to compare lengths.

**Teacher:** I'm wondering how you compared different objects to the tower of ten. Did anyone find a way you think works well?

**Yoshio:** I put them on the table next to each other.

**Teacher:** Can you say a little more about that? Let's see, if you were comparing the tray to the tower, you would put them on the table next to each other—like this?

**Yoshio:** [rearranging the objects] No, next to each other the other way. Like this. See? The tray is longer. It goes up and down (beyond the tower at both ends).

**Teacher:** Oh, I see. So you put the tower next to the long side of the tray [traces the long edge of the tray with a finger] and the tray was longer than the tower. Did anyone else do it like Yoshio? [Several students raise their hands.]

**Teacher:** Did anyone do it a different way? Would someone compare the tray and the tower a different way?

**Jack:** I did it like your first way.

**Teacher:** Can you show us?

**Jack:** Like this. The tower was taller on top and on the bottom.

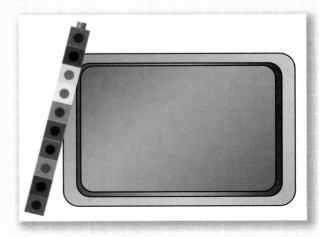

**Teacher:** Interesting! So, this way, the tray is *shorter* than the tower. What does everyone think about that? Does it matter how you lay the tray?

**Lisa:** Doesn't it need to be straight?

**Teacher:** What do people think? Does it matter if the things you are comparing are straight?

**Jack:** [He adjusts the tower to make it straight but does not line up the end with one edge of the tray.] It doesn't matter. See? The tower's the same—taller on top and on the bottom.

[Other students agree with Jack that "straightness" doesn't matter.]

**Teacher:** So some of you think it matters if the tower is straight and some of you don't. Let's keep that question in mind as we do more measuring and comparing. We'll continue to think and talk about it together.

**Teacher:** Does someone have another way to compare the tower to the tray?

**Cindy:** I did it sorta the same as Yoshio, but I put the cubes down more, right on the edge of the table. [She adjusts the arrangement again.] Then you look to see which goes up more. So it was only taller on top.

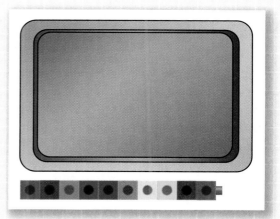

**Teacher:** So Cindy put them next to each other on the table too, just like Yoshio, but she lined up the bottoms of the two things. Did anyone else use this strategy too? [Some students raise hands.] Any other methods for comparing these two?

**Manuel:** I didn't lay them down. I stood them up, like this. Then you can tell the tray is longer because it's taller up. [He demonstrates but has a hard time standing the tray on its edge.] This tray doesn't do it so good. It worked good with the bottle and the box though.

**Teacher:** Does that way remind anyone of another way we heard about? It reminds me a little bit of Cindy's way. What's the same about them?

This exchange reflects the range of ideas—both accurate and inaccurate—that exist when young students begin to explore measuring. Expect such situations to arise in your classroom, and do not rush to show students how to measure "correctly." Students learn the important ideas in measuring gradually over time and with repeated experiences. You can facilitate their learning by encouraging them to share their strategies and explain their thinking.

# You Have to Look at the Long Side

These students have been working at the Measuring Table, comparing lengths of objects to a tower of ten cubes and placing the objects in groups longer than the tower or shorter than the tower. Observing that certain objects have been placed differently by different students—sometimes in the longer group and sometimes in the shorter group—the teacher decides to discuss one such item in Session 2.2, a book that is short and wide.

**Teacher:** I was at the Measuring Table the other day, and I saw something really interesting. First, I saw someone take this book, compare it to the tower, and put it in the group of things that were longer than the tower. Then I saw another person compare this book to a tower and put it in the other group—things that were *shorter* than a tower. Did anyone have any trouble with this book that they'd like to share?

**Sarah:** Well, I did this book and I found out that it was longer than my tower. But then Tammy did the same book and she said it was shorter. It can't be both. I think I'm right.

**Teacher:** What do people think about that? Is that okay? Can an object be in one group one time and in the other group another time?

**Timothy:** I don't think so, because it's the same thing. It didn't grow or get smaller or change or anything.

**Teacher:** Maybe if the two of you could show us how you compared your tower to this book, that would help.

**Sarah:** I did it like this. See? It's longer than my tower.

**Teacher:** Tammy, would you like to show us how you compared the tower and the book? Or, actually, can anyone think of a way that Tammy might have compared this tower and this book and found out that the tower was longer?

**Victor:** I think she did it like me. See, Sarah held the book like this. But when you read the book, you hold it like this. So that way, the tower is way longer than the book.

**Teacher:** So does it matter which way you hold the book?

**Tammy:** It matters for when you read it.

**Sarah:** It matters for reading it. But I think when you measure it, you have to look at the long side and put that by your tower.

**Teacher:** So for some objects, there is more than one side that can be measured. I wonder if that's true for every object?

# Dialogue Box

# Playing *Compare* with a Partner

The students in this class have just finished playing the game of *Compare* for the first time. The teacher gathers them together at the end of Session 2.5 to discuss issues that often arise when students work in partners.

**Teacher:** Today you played *Compare* with a partner. We are going to be playing a lot of math games this year. When you play a game, it's important that you learn a lot and enjoy yourself. I'm wondering, what are some things that make a good partnership?

**Kiyo:** No fighting.

**Emma:** No saying, "I won! I won!"

**Dennis:** No cheating.

**Teacher:** What things could you do to be helpful?

**Jae:** If someone can't count, help them.

**Mia:** Say, "Good job."

**Lionel:** Take turns.

**Teacher:** Those are some helpful suggestions. Keep those things in mind while I play with Kiyo. [The teacher whispers her plan in Kiyo's ear.] Watch closely and listen carefully . . . [The teacher deals a seven; Kiyo gets a three.] Whoo hoo! Me!! I win!! . . . What do you think about how I was playing?

**Victor:** That wasn't nice. You might make Kiyo feel bad.

**Teacher:** What could I do instead?

**Tammy:** You could let Kiyo be the winner.

**Teacher:** Letting Kiyo say "me" might make her feel good, but in this game it is the person with the higher number who says "me."

**Lisa:** You could just say "me" and then "maybe you will get it next time."

Next, the teacher asks Latoya to be her partner. She whispers her plan to Latoya and they play several rounds. Each time, the teacher quickly says who has the higher card. Latoya is silent.

**Teacher:** What do you think about how I was playing with Latoya?

**Lionel:** You never gave Latoya a chance! That's not fair.

**Teacher:** What could I have done instead?

**Lionel:** You could have waited. She could have said sometimes, too, who was higher.

**Teacher:** Ricardo, can you play with me? This time there is something you are going to do, too.

The teacher whispers into Ricardo's ear and then they each turn over a card. The teacher tries to count the pictures on the card, but keeps losing track and saying more than one number per object.

**Ricardo:** You could maybe get some cubes. That might help you count.

**Teacher:** What do you think about what Ricardo did when he played with me?

**Beth:** He was helpful! He told you something that might help you.

The teacher plays one more round, with Beth. The teacher gets a six and Beth gets a nine.

**Beth:** Me.

**Teacher:** Nuh unh! You're wrong! Mine's bigger!!! . . . [She looks to students for comments.]

**Kiyo:** You weren't very nice. You should have just believed her.

**Teacher:** What if I really did think my number was bigger?

**Jae:** You could say, "I think my number is bigger."

**Teacher:** And then what could we do? What if Beth and I really don't agree on whose number is bigger? What could we do about that?

**Sarah:** You could both count them again and watch the other person count.

**Kyle:** You could look on the number line.

**Teacher:** How could the number line help?

**Kyle:** You could see which number's more that way (points to the right). That means it's bigger.

**Mia:** You could build with cubes like in that *Grab and Count* game and see which one is taller.

**Teacher:** Those are some good ideas about what to try if you disagree with your partner.

Working with a partner is an important but often challenging part of working cooperatively on math activities in Kindergarten. This teacher helps students problem-solve difficulties that have (or may) come up by role-playing interactions within the game of *Compare*. The discussion addresses both social and mathematical problems, as students brainstorm ways to be helpful partners and to deal with disagreements about which quantity is larger.

# Comparing and Ordering Towers

This teacher is introducing *Grab and Count: Ordering* to the class in Session 2.10. A volunteer has grabbed four handfuls of cubes and built four towers.

**Teacher:** Now we have four towers in four different colors. I'm going to line them up next to each other. What do you notice? What can you tell me about these towers?

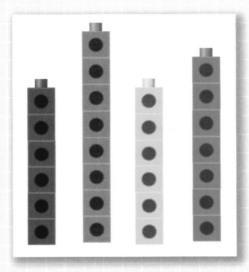

**Carmen:** They go red, orange, yellow, green.

**Jason:** They look like a rainbow.

**Teacher:** Can you compare them? Do some towers have more cubes than others?

**Kyle:** The green one has more than the yellow one. See how it goes up one higher?

**Ricardo:** Red and yellow have the same, 1, 2, 3, 4, 5, 6.

**Teacher:** So she grabbed six cubes twice.

**Jason:** Red is the smallest.

**Jennifer:** Well, red's tied with yellow, so they're both the smallest. [She places the red tower next to the yellow to compare them, then counts the cubes in each tower to check.] Yup. Six is the smallest.

**Teacher:** So the smallest handfuls had six cubes. What else do you notice?

**Hugo:** Orange is the most. It's the tallest.

**Kyle:** Yeah. It's two taller.

**Teacher:** Can you show us what you mean?

**Kyle:** [puts the orange and red towers next to each other] The red is two steps away from the orange.

**Hugo:** Two dots away [referring to the circles on the cube faces].

**Teacher:** What if we wanted to put these towers in order? Does anyone have an idea about how to do that?

**Raul:** I know! You, umm. . . umm. . . What do you mean, *in order?*

**Teacher:** What if we wanted to line them up so that they went from smallest to biggest? How might you do that?

**Abby:** Just look at them. Make them like stairs.

**Teacher:** Can you show us what you mean?

**Abby:** Well, this one is short and so is yellow. They're a tie. Like a bottom step of the stairs. Then green is a little bit bigger and orange wins. [She arranges cubes in the order shown.]

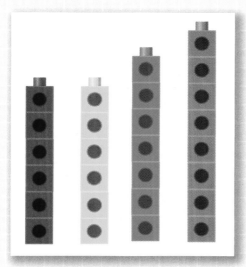

**Teacher:** So Abby looked at the towers and thought about stairs. Can everyone see how these remind Abby of stairs? Would anybody put the towers in order in a different way?

**Brad:** You could trade the yellow and red. [He does this and sits back.] That's a different way.

**Teacher:** Interesting. Brad switched the towers that were the same. Are the towers still in order? [The students agree.] Why can he do that?

**Abby:** Because they're the same.

**Brad:** Yeah, they're both the smallest. They both have six so it doesn't matter.

**Teacher:** [Mixes the four towers again.] Would anyone put the towers in order a different way? How would you start?

**Sarah:** Well, I'd put the same ones together.

**Teacher:** The same ones? Can you show me which ones you mean?

**Sarah:** This one is the same as this one [she holds the yellow up to the red, then lays them together off to the side.] And this one is the same as [holds the orange up to the green]. . . nope. They don't match. Orange is bigger.

**Teacher:** I see now what you mean by putting "same ones" together. What would you do next, to put them in order?

**Sarah:** These are the smallest. This one has [silently counts the cubes in the yellow tower] . . . six. [Next she counts the red tower.] So does this one. [She lays red next to the yellow.] Green is [she counts silently] seven, so it goes next, and the big one has [counts to herself again] . . . eight.

**Teacher:** So Sarah put towers next to each other. She put ones that were the same together, and then I noticed that she counted how many cubes were in the towers to help her put them in order. Does anyone have a different way to put these towers in order?

When this discussion began, students were describing data, making comparisons, and talking about the ideas more than, less than, and equal to. They used these relationships later as they discussed how to put the cubes in order, a new concept for many of the students.

# Student Math Handbook

The *Student Math Handbook* pages related to this unit are pictured on the following pages. This book is designed to be used flexibly: as a resource for students doing classwork, as a book students can take home for reference while doing homework and playing math games with their families, and as a reference for families to better understand the work their children are doing in class.

## How Many? (0, 1, 2)

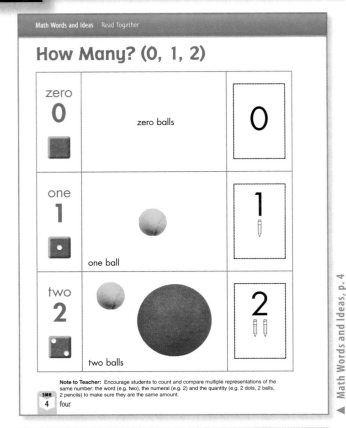

zero
0

zero balls

0

one
1

one ball

1

two
2

two balls

2

**Note to Teacher:** Encourage students to count and compare multiple representations of the same number: the word (e.g. two), the numeral (e.g. 2) and the quantity (e.g. 2 dots, 2 balls, 2 pencils) to make sure they are the same amount.

SMH 4 four

◀ Math Words and Ideas, p. 4

## How Many? (3, 4)

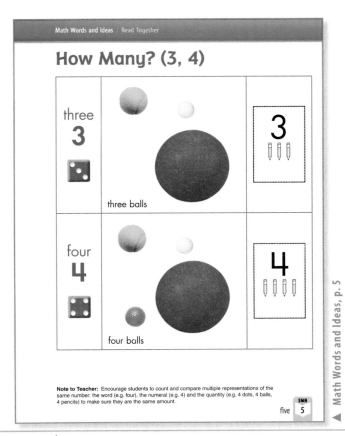

three
3

three balls

3

four
4

four balls

4

**Note to Teacher:** Encourage students to count and compare multiple representations of the same number: the word (e.g. four), the numeral (e.g. 4) and the quantity (e.g. 4 dots, 4 balls, 4 pencils) to make sure they are the same amount.

five SMH 5

◀ Math Words and Ideas, p. 5

## How Many? (5, 6)

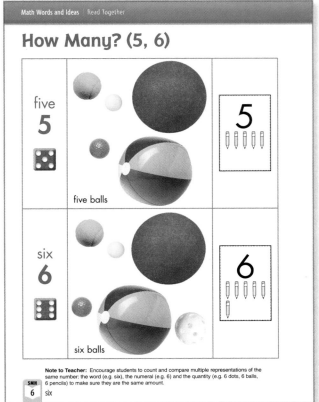

five
5

five balls

5

six
6

six balls

6

**Note to Teacher:** Encourage students to count and compare multiple representations of the same number: the word (e.g. six), the numeral (e.g. 6) and the quantity (e.g. 6 dots, 6 balls, 6 pencils) to make sure they are the same amount.

SMH 6 six

◀ Math Words and Ideas, p. 6

## Math Words and Ideas | Read Together

# How Many? (7)

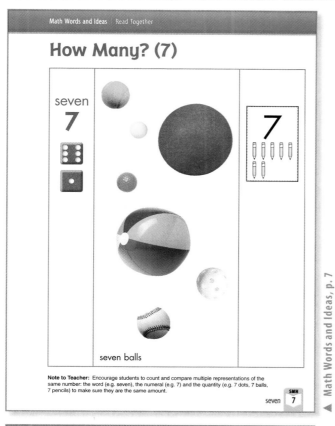

seven
7

seven balls

7

Note to Teacher: Encourage students to count and compare multiple representations of the same number: the word (e.g. seven), the numeral (e.g. 7) and the quantity (e.g. 7 dots, 7 balls, 7 pencils) to make sure they are the same amount.

SMH
seven 7

◄ Math Words and Ideas, p. 7

## Math Words and Ideas | Read Together

# How Many? (8)

eight
8

eight balls

8

Note to Teacher: Encourage students to count and compare multiple representations of the same number: the word (e.g. eight), the numeral (e.g. 8) and the quantity (e.g. 8 dots, 8 balls, 8 pencils) to make sure they are the same amount.

SMH
8 eight

◄ Math Words and Ideas, p. 8

## Math Words and Ideas | Read Together

# How Many? (9)

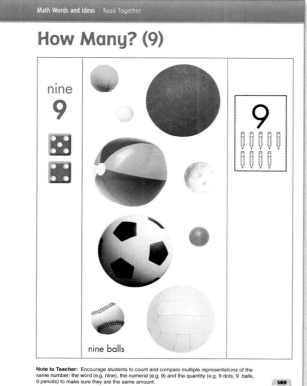

nine
9

nine balls

9

Note to Teacher: Encourage students to count and compare multiple representations of the same number: the word (e.g. nine), the numeral (e.g. 9) and the quantity (e.g. 9 dots, 9 balls, 9 pencils) to make sure they are the same amount.

SMH
nine 9

◄ Math Words and Ideas, p. 9

## Math Words and Ideas | Read Together

# How Many? (10)

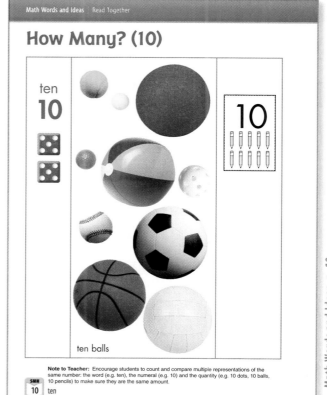

ten
10

ten balls

10

Note to Teacher: Encourage students to count and compare multiple representations of the same number: the word (e.g. ten), the numeral (e.g. 10) and the quantity (e.g. 10 dots, 10 balls, 10 pencils) to make sure they are the same amount.

SMH
10 ten

◄ Math Words and Ideas, p. 10

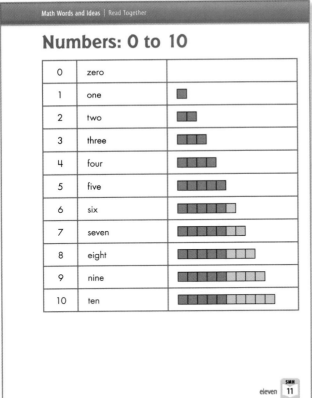

Math Words and Ideas, p. 11

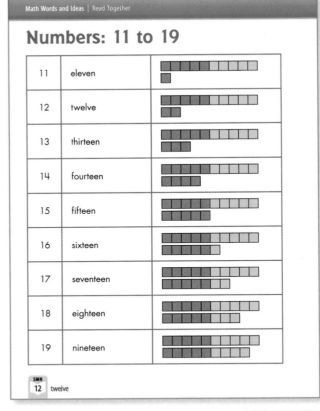

Math Words and Ideas, p. 12

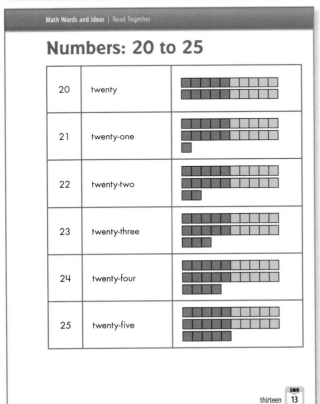

Math Words and Ideas, p. 13

# Counting

People count every day. They count to find out how many.

How many balls?

1   2   3

4   5   6   7

8   9   10

10 balls

**? When do you count? What do you like to count?**

**Note to Teacher:** Because counting is the foundation for much of the number work that Kindergarteners do, encourage them to discuss why they count.

seventeen   SMH 17

◄ Math Words and Ideas, p. 17

---

# More Counting

How many students are here today?

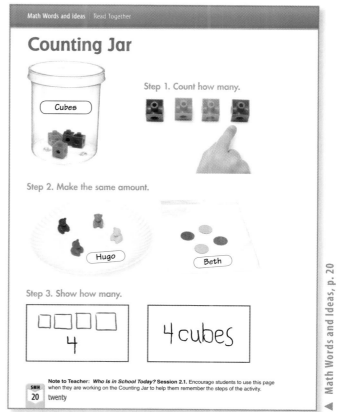

20 students are here today.

**? How many students are in your class?**

**Note to Teacher:** *Who Is in School Today?* **Session 1.1.** Use this page to show that we use numbers both to count a set of objects (1, 2, 3, . . . 20) and to describe the quantity of those objects (the total is 20).

SMH 18   eighteen

◄ Math Words and Ideas, p. 18

---

# Ways to Count

When you count, you say one number for each object. You need to keep track of what you are counting.

The last number you say is the total. The total tells you how many are in the group.

Look at how some children count.

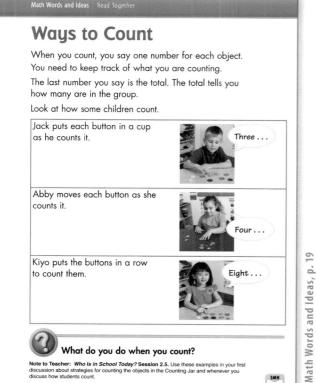

| | |
|---|---|
| Jack puts each button in a cup as he counts it. | Three . . . |
| Abby moves each button as she counts it. | Four . . . |
| Kiyo puts the buttons in a row to count them. | Eight . . . |

**? What do you do when you count?**

**Note to Teacher:** *Who Is in School Today?* **Session 2.5.** Use these examples in your first discussion about strategies for counting the objects in the Counting Jar and whenever you discuss how students count.

nineteen   SMH 19

◄ Math Words and Ideas, p. 19

---

# Counting Jar

Cubes

Step 1. Count how many.

Step 2. Make the same amount.

Hugo

Beth

Step 3. Show how many.

☐☐☐☐
4

4 cubes

**Note to Teacher:** *Who Is in School Today?* **Session 2.1.** Encourage students to use this page when they are working on the Counting Jar to help them remember the steps of the activity.

SMH 20   twenty

◄ Math Words and Ideas, p. 20

---

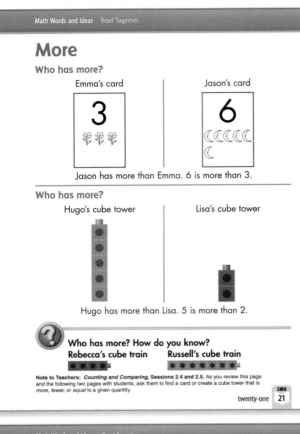

### More

**Who has more?**

Emma's card

3

Jason's card

6

Jason has more than Emma. 6 is more than 3.

**Who has more?**

Hugo's cube tower

Lisa's cube tower

Hugo has more than Lisa. 5 is more than 2.

**? Who has more? How do you know?**
Rebecca's cube train          Russell's cube train

*Note to Teachers: Counting and Comparing, Sessions 2.4 and 2.5. As you review this page and the following two pages with students, ask them to find a card or create a cube tower that is more, fewer, or equal to a given quantity.*

twenty-one **SMH 21**

Math Words and Ideas, p. 21

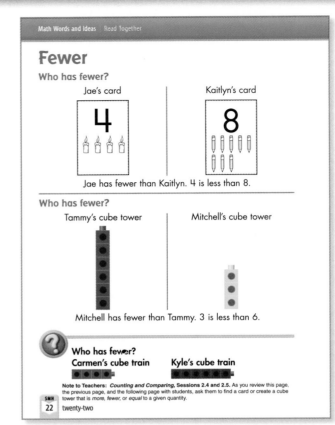

### Fewer

**Who has fewer?**

Jae's card

4

Kaitlyn's card

8

Jae has fewer than Kaitlyn. 4 is less than 8.

**Who has fewer?**

Tammy's cube tower

Mitchell's cube tower

Mitchell has fewer than Tammy. 3 is less than 6.

**? Who has fewer?**
Carmen's cube train          Kyle's cube train

*Note to Teachers: Counting and Comparing, Sessions 2.4 and 2.5. As you review this page, the previous page, and the following page with students, ask them to find a card or create a cube tower that is more, fewer, or equal to a given quantity.*

**SMH 22** twenty-two

Math Words and Ideas, p. 22

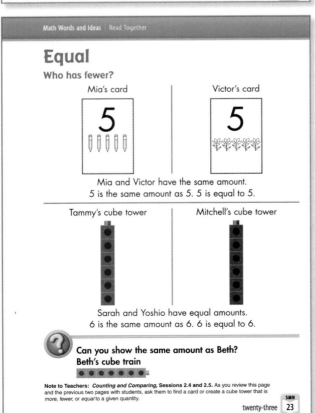

### Equal

**Who has fewer?**

Mia's card

5

Victor's card

5

Mia and Victor have the same amount.
5 is the same amount as 5. 5 is equal to 5.

Tammy's cube tower

Mitchell's cube tower

Sarah and Yoshio have equal amounts.
6 is the same amount as 6. 6 is equal to 6.

**? Can you show the same amount as Beth?**
Beth's cube train

*Note to Teachers: Counting and Comparing, Sessions 2.4 and 2.5. As you review this page and the previous two pages with students, ask them to find a card or create a cube tower that is more, fewer, or equal to a given quantity.*

twenty-three **SMH 23**

Math Words and Ideas, p. 23

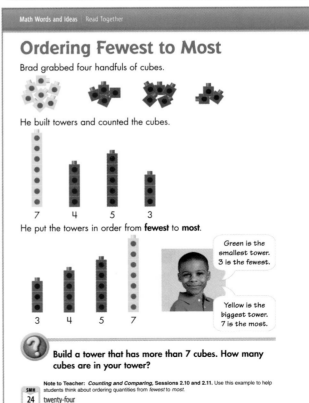

## Ordering Fewest to Most

Brad grabbed four handfuls of cubes.

He built towers and counted the cubes.

7          4          5          3

He put the towers in order from **fewest** to **most**.

3          4          5          7

Green is the smallest tower. 3 is the fewest.

Yellow is the biggest tower. 7 is the most.

**? Build a tower that has more than 7 cubes. How many cubes are in your tower?**

*Note to Teacher: Counting and Comparing, Sessions 2.10 and 2.11. Use this example to help students think about ordering quantities from fewest to most.*

**SMH 24** twenty-four

Math Words and Ideas, p. 24

# Shorter or Longer

These students used a tower of 10 cubes to measure some objects in their classroom.

Some objects were **shorter** than the 10 cubes.
Some objects were **longer** than the 10 cubes.

**Shorter**

This crayon is shorter.

My hand is shorter.

**Longer**

This book is longer.

My arm is longer.

**?** What can you find that is shorter than 10 cubes?
What can you find that is longer than 10 cubes?

**Note to Teacher:** *Counting and Comparing*, **Session 2.1.** Students can consider these visual representations of the concepts of **shorter** and **longer** either before or after they have looked for objects that are shorter or longer than ten cubes.

thirty-seven **SMH 37**

▲ Math Words and Ideas, p. 37

# Index